BIVALVE FILTER FEEDING:
HYDRODYNAMICS, BIOENERGETICS,
PHYSIOLOGY AND ECOLOGY

C. BARKER JØRGENSEN

Bivalve Filter Feeding:

Hydrodynamics, Bioenergetics, Physiology and Ecology

OLSEN & OLSEN

1990

This book is dedicated to

HANS ULRIK RIISGÅRD
POUL SCHEEL LARSEN
FLEMMING MØHLENBERG

BIVALVE FILTER FEEDING:
HYDRODYNAMICS, BIOENERGETICS, PHYSIOLOGY AND ECOLOGY
by C. Barker Jørgensen

Copyright © C. Barker Jørgensen 1990

Olsen & Olsen, Helstedsvej 10, DK-3480 Fredensborg, Denmark
ISBN 87-85215-20-1

Contents

Preface

Herbivory in aquatic ecosystems implies feeding on suspended unicellular plants, the phytoplankton. Animals that feed on suspended particles in the ambient water are collectively known as filter feeders. Filter-feeding bivalves constitute a predominant component of many benthic ecosystems, and ecological and economic importance, combined with an apparent robustness as experimental animals, have made bivalves favourites in studies of filter feeding.

Almost a quarter of a century ago I dealt monographically with the biology of suspension feeding (Jørgensen, 1966). I arrived at the conclusion that suspension feeding tends to develop a high degree of automaticity, characterized by a continuous transport at a constant rate of a feeding current to structures that retain suspended particles without regard to their value as food. Thus, the rate of accumulation of food in the feeding structures is not regulated according to the actual need of the individual, but is basically determined by the fixed rates at which water is filtered, by the concentration of food particles in the water, and by the efficiency with which these particles are retained in the feeding structures.

In the intervening decades this conclusion has been challenged by investigators of filter feeding, particularly in bivalves, and presently the view predominates that filter-feeding bivalves do regulate their food intake. However, the evidence for interpretations in terms of regulation of feeding is ambiguous, and physiological mechanisms for such regulation have remained unknown. The author and his collaborators therefore focused on the elucidation of mechanisms of feeding in filter-feeding bivalves and on the factors that determine the rate of filtration. The perspective spans from the fluid mechanics that governs the processing of the ambient water in the filter pump to the ecology and evolution of suspension feeding. It is felt that the results obtained warrant a reappraisal of the biology of bivalve filter feeding.

I am much obliged to the following who critically read and greatly improved the manuscript: Michael Depledge, Thomas Kiørboe, Poul Scheel Larsen, Flemming Møhlenberg and Hans Ulrik Riisgård. I thank Lis Christensen for typing the manuscript.

[1]

Introduction

Filter feeding is an adaptation allowing animals to feed on suspended microscopic food particles that cannot be sensed and seized individually. Such food particles are primarily the unicellular phytoplankton that constitute the major primary producers in the sea and all but the smallest and shallowest lakes. Filter feeders pump the ambient water through filters that retain suspended matter, usually irrespective of whether this matter is of food value or not. In the following this is referred to as water processing.

The concentration of suspended food particles in aquatic environments is mostly low, in the order of 1 mg or less of organic matter per litre of water. Suspension feeders must therefore process large amounts of water to meet their food requirements.

By their filtering activity suspension feeders may greatly affect their habitats. They may act as biodepositors of silt and detritus, and they may control primary production by grazing the phytoplankton. The effect of grazing on phytoplankton production and standing crop has been extensively studied and discussed for planktonic pelagic ecosystems in terms of zooplankton–phytoplankton interrelationships (Andersen *et al.*, 1987; Dagg & Turner, 1982; Jackson, 1980; Longhurst, 1976; McCauley & Briand, 1979; Nicolajsen *et al.*, 1983; Timms & Moss, 1984; Welschmeyer & Lorenzen, 1985). The greatest impact on the environment is, however, observed in benthic filter-feeding communities, such as sponges on coral reefs (Buss & Jackson, 1981; Reiswig, 1973, 1974) and mussel beds within the intertidal or sublittoral zones (Dame & Dankers, 1988; B.B. Jørgensen, 1980; C.B. Jørgensen, 1984). In coastal waters dense populations of filter-feeding bivalves may play important roles in the control of phytoplankton production (Cloern, 1982; Cohen *et al.*, 1984; Officer *et al.*, 1982).

The relations between filter-feeding bivalves and the ambient water extend to dissolved organic molecules which may be taken up through the epidermis. The uptake is facilitated by the large surface presented by the gills and the large volumes of water the filtration process brings into contact with the surfaces (Jørgensen, 1983b; Manahan *et al.*, 1983; Stephens, 1988; Wright,

[3]

1987). Molecules absorbed may also include toxic elements derived from a polluting environment and the absorbed material may accumulate in the bivalve body. This ability of filter-feeding bivalves to concentrate toxic elements present in the ambient water is the basis for their use as pollution monitors. Because of their wide geographical distribution the mussels *Mytilus* and *Perna* spp. have obtained international status as universal pollution indicators.

The importance of filter-feeding bivalves in benthic communities, in pollution control, as well as in aquaculture, explains the great interest in their biology in general and in feeding and water processing in particular.

CHAPTER I

Functional morphology of bivalve feeding

Investigations of the feeding mechanisms in filter-feeding bivalves rest on an old tradition that has changed only little until recent years, when generally accepted concepts of ciliary filter feeding are being questioned.

Early in the 19th century, Sharpey (1830, 1836) gave a remarkably accurate account of the structure and function of the bivalve gill. Based on microscopical observations of living gills, especially in *Mytilus edulis*, he recognized the main ciliary tracts on the gill filaments and their functions in producing water currents and collecting food particles. Sharpey identified the three main tracts of cilia on the filaments, later to be known as frontal cilia, laterofrontal cirri and lateral cilia. The latter he observed to beat metachronally. The frontal cilia he ascribed the function of transporting retained food particles to the margin of the gill along which ciliary tracts carried the particles further on towards the mouth, whereas the lateral cilia produced the water currents through the interfilament canals of the gills. Sharpey believed that the laterofrontal cirri also participated in producing the through current.

Without referring to Sharpey's studies on the ciliation of the mussel gill, Alder & Hancock (1851) gave an equally remarkably correct description of filter feeding in *Mya* and *Pholas*. They demonstrated the inhalant and exhalant water currents, and thus the function of the siphons, by means of indigo-coloured sea water, and they noted that the exhaled coloured fluid was deprived of particles. This observation led to further studies of the structure and function of the gills, which were shown to act both in producing the ciliary through current and in filtering the water, other cilia transporting the retained particles towards the mouth. Alder & Hancock confirmed this sieve-like nature of the gills and their mode of action also in other bivalve types, and they assumed that the mechanisms applied to filter-feeding bivalves generally.

At the turn of the century gill structure and ciliation of the filaments had been described in more than 200 species of bivalves (Janssens, 1893; Ridewood, 1903). But the importance and way of functioning of the gill as an organ of feeding long remained a matter of discussion (Bonnet, 1877; Herdman, 1904; Kellogg, 1892; Pelseneer, 1906). The role of the bivalve gill as the primary organ of water transport and collection of food was finally established by Wallengren (1905a,b) in studies on *Anodonta* sp., *Mytilus edulis* and *Mya arenaria*.

Subsequent work on feeding in bivalves has largely consisted in observations made on preparations of animals with one valve and mantle removed, on isolated gills and gill fragments, as well as on excised labial palps. The main emphasis has been on description of patterns of ciliary tracts on the gill filaments and on the palps in different types of bivalves. Ciliary tracts and their function were studied by means of suspended particles of various kinds dropped onto the surface of gills and palps. Some outstanding early contributions to this field of study of bivalve feeding are those of Kellogg (1915), Orton (1912) and Yonge (1923-24, 1926-27).

Studies of this type culminated in the work of Atkins (1936, 1937a,b) who described the ciliary tracts on the frontal surface of the gill filaments in some 90 species of bivalves. She established the classification of gill types, mainly based on patterns of ciliary tracts, that is still extensively used. To Atkins and her successors, sorting of particles was the key concept to the understanding of the feeding mechanism in filter-feeding bivalves. It was assumed that sorting mechanisms were best demonstrated by the use of dense particles, such as carborundum powder, because they ensured that the particles were 'actually in contact with the cilia, and thus moved by them and not by some superficial water current' (Atkins, 1936, p. 185).

Atkins emphasized the importance of distinguishing between two main types of frontal ciliary tracts: the lateral tracts of fine cilia which were thought to preferentially carry small and light particles, and the median tract

[5]

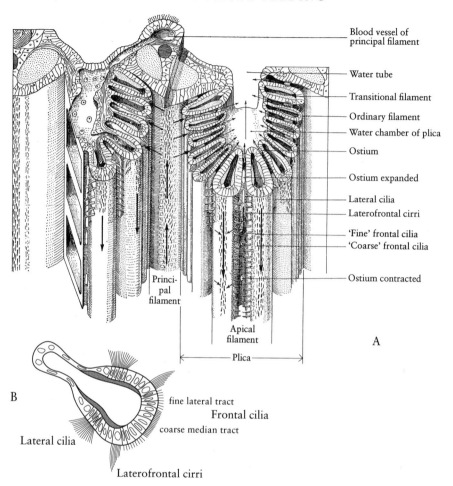

Blood vessel of
principal filament

Water tube

Transitional filament

Ordinary filament

Water chamber of plica

Ostium

Ostium expanded

Lateral cilia

Laterofrontal cirri

'Fine' frontal cilia

'Coarse' frontal cilia

Ostium contracted

Princi-
pal
filament

Apical
filament

Plica

A

B

fine lateral tract

Frontal cilia

coarse median tract

Lateral cilia

Laterofrontal cirri

Figure 1. A: Diagram of a plicate gill (oyster), showing one plica and a half with connecting principal filament along which the ciliary current is towards the dorsal margin of the gill. The filaments of a plica are differentiated into the transitional filament next to the principal filament, ordinary filaments constituting the plical sides and the apical filaments of the plical creast. On the plical filaments two types of frontal ciliary tracts are distinguished, termed coarse median tract and fine lateral tracts bounded by the laterofrontal cirri. Water chamber of plica and water tube are parts of the suprabranchial cavity, into which leads the ostia, which may be expanded or contracted. Arrows indicate direction of surface currents and through currents (redrawn from Nelson, 1960). B: Diagram of transverse section of a gill filament showing the differentiation of the frontal cilia into the coarse median tract and fine lateral tracts (redrawn from Owen & McCrae, 1976).

[6]

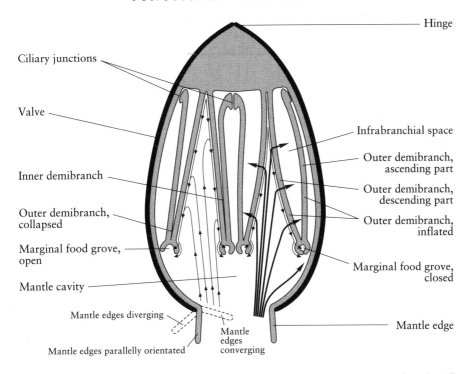

Figure 2. Diagram of cross section of mussel, indicating main water currents when the gill transports water both through the interfilament canals and along the frontal surface of the gill filaments (right side of diagram, demibranchs are inflated) and when only the frontal surface of the filaments transports water (left side of diagram, demibranchs collapsed). Heavy lines indicate strong water currents; fine lines, weak currents. Currents are only shown between an outer and an inner demibranch. The diagram also illustrates shapes of the marginal groove from closed to widely open, as well as the varying orientation of the mantle edges in fully open animals (from Jørgensen, 1975a).

of coarse cilia, believed to carry large and heavy particles (Figure 1). The fine tracts terminate in food grooves along the dorsal and/or ventral margins of the gills, and they constitute acceptance tracts that select potential food particles in the processing of the ambient water. The coarse tracts lead to the ventral margin of the gills where they continue into other coarse tracts, the terminal frontal cilia, situated outside the food groove (Figure 2). Mostly, the fine ciliary tracts were observed to be constantly active, whereas the coarse tracts were only active when stimulated by the presence of coarse or heavy particles. Moreover, heavy particles stimulated profuse secretion of

[7]

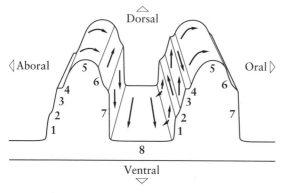

Figure 3. Diagram of two folds on the inner face of the palps of a member of the Ungulinidae or Thyasiridae showing the direction of beat of the cilia of the eight tracts (from Allen, 1958).

mucus that consolidated the particles. But fine particles were also assumed to be embedded in mucus to assure their transport along the tracts of fine cilia.

In some bivalve genera the tracts of terminal frontal cilia run posteriorly and the material they carry is dropped onto the mantle surface and eliminated as pseudofaeces, e.g., *Arca* and *Anomia*. In these genera the coarse tracts are thus definitive rejection tracts. In most genera, however, the tracts run anteriorly and the material carried by the tracts is transferred onto the labial palps.

The inner side of the labial palps is folded (Figure 3) and already Wallengren (1905b) observed that these folds are furnished with complex systems of ciliary tracts. He described sorting of particles according to size, so that small particles were preferentially carried towards the mouth and large particles along rejection tracts. Later, the importance of the labial palps in bivalve feeding, especially in sorting of material collected by the gills, was specifically studied and stressed by Kellogg (1915), Graham (1931), Allen (1958) and Ansell (1961). Allen (1958) attempted a synthesis of features

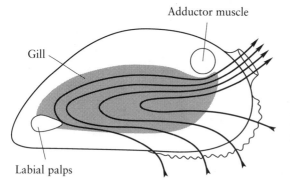

Figure 4. Diagram of water current passing through the mantle cavity in a mussel with extended mantle edges and exhalant siphon (from Jørgensen et al., 1986a).

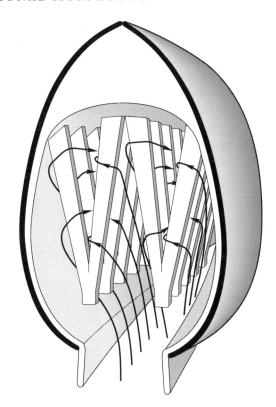

Figure 5. Spatial presentation of pattern of currents through mantle cavity and gills. For clarity only two demibranchs are drawn. The current enters through the inhalant aperture, as indicated in Figure 4, disperses into numerous microcurrents at the level of the interfilament canals, and unites again in the suprabranchial cavity and the exhalant siphon (from Jørgensen *et al.*, 1986a).

that were common to all bivalves, and he distinguished between acceptance tracts running across the ridges of the palp folds towards the mouth, rejection tracts running in the bottom of the troughs between the folds, and re-sorting tracts along the aboral sides of the folds (Figure 3).

From the large number of studies of how preparations of gills and palps deal with particles of various kinds and sizes, a mucociliary mechanism of bivalve feeding emerged that may be summarized as follows. A flow of water is maintained through the mantle cavity and the gills by means of the activity of the lateral cilia (Figures 4 and 5). The water is filtered at the entrance to the interfilament canals by the laterofrontal cirri which both strain particles from the water and throw them onto the frontal surface of the filaments. The particles adhere to mucus, secreted by numerous gland cells on the filaments. The mucus-embedded particles are carried by frontal ciliary tracts to the ventral and/or dorsal margins of the gills and farther towards the

[9]

mouth. The material transported along dorsal ciliary tracts reaches the mouth directly, whereas material transported along the ventral margins is taken up by the labial palps where ciliary tracts on the inner surfaces carry out the final sorting of material for acceptance or rejection.

The tradition in the studies of the functional morphology of bivalve feeding structures, established in the thirties, has continued up to the present time (Owen, 1953; Purchon, 1954, 1955a,b; Clausen, 1958; Allen, 1958, 1968; Nelson, 1960; Stasek, 1962; Morton, 1969, 1970, 1976; Fankboner, 1971; Judd, 1971; Narchi, 1972; Hughes, 1975; Lam, 1977; Ansell, 1981).

CHAPTER II

Ciliary feeding and fluid mechanics

The mucociliary concept of feeding in bivalves was developed without consideration of physical constraints imposed by low Reynolds number fluid dynamics that applies to suspension processing in filter feeders (Jørgensen, 1983a).

The Reynolds number Re is given by the relation $Re = \rho l v / \eta$, where ρ is the density of the fluid, l is a characteristic length, e.g., a diameter of a tube or dimension of a particle, v is the velocity and η is the dynamic viscosity. Re is thus a dimensionless number that expresses the ratio between inertial forces and viscous forces. This implies that a flow is laminar, with orderly streamlines, when the Reynolds number is less than a certain critical value, e.g., 2300 for pipe flow (Walshaw & Jobson, 1979, p.288). Above this value the flow is unstable and becomes turbulent. Furthermore, when $Re < 1$ inertial effects are negligible. Physical dimensions and fluid velocities are normally so small in filter-feeding animals that we always deal with laminar flow, and in ciliary feeding the flow is creeping, $Re \ll 1$.

The parameter characterizing the motion of a suspended particle is the Stokesian time constant, $t_p = (d_p^2 / 18 v)(\rho_p / \rho_f)$, where d_p denotes the equivalent spherical diameter of the particle, $v = \eta / \rho_f$ the kinematic viscosity of the fluid, ρ_p the density of the particle, and ρ_f the density of the fluid (Soo, 1967, p.33).

[10]

The constant t_p is a measure of the time it takes the particle, if initially at rest, to be accelerated to the fluid velocity. Similarly, t_p is a measure for the time it takes a particle to come to rest if the fluid is suddenly brought to rest. For a 10 µm-diameter particle in water, $t_p \approx 10^{-6}$ s, hence such particles will closely follow the instantaneous fluid motion as long as this is characterized by times that are orders of magnitude greater, which is normally the case. For example, a flow curving with radius 40 µm and velocity 1 mm s^{-1} has a characteristic time of $40 \cdot 10^{-6}/1 \cdot 10^{-3} = 4 \cdot 10^{-2}$ s, which is four orders of magnitude greater than t_p.

Investigators of filter feeding do not usually directly refer to the physical conditions applying, but mechanisms suggested reveal that observations made on particle movements have been interpreted in terms of 'macroscopic world' physics, dominated by inertial forces (Purcell, 1977; Vogel, 1981). This is evident, e.g., when it is implied that inertial momentum governs particle movements. Thus, particles are said to 'impinge' on ciliated surfaces when the flow directed towards the surface is deflected, leaving the water depleted of particles (Atkins, 1936; Bernard, 1974a; Bullivant, 1968; Foster-Smith, 1975; Fretter & Montgommery, 1968; Gilmour, 1979; Stebbing & Dilly, 1972; Werner, 1955). Other cilia, such as the laterofrontal cirri of the bivalve gill filaments, are said to intercept particles in the through current and to 'throw' or 'flick' particles onto the frontal surface of the filaments (Morton, 1969, 1983; Yonge, 1926-1927).

Such statements imply that particles come into physical contact with the cilia and that the stroke that hits a particle conveys inertial momentum to the particle, momentum that carries it across streamlines to land on and thus to obtain contact with the cilia of the frontal tracts. It is moreover implied, and often explicitly stated, that the physical impact of particles hitting the frontal surface of the gill filaments stimulates the secretion of mucus that is needed to bind the particles.

When large particles of high density enter through the inhalant opening of oysters and other bivalves they have been assumed to settle on the inner mantle surface before they reach the gill, a gravimetric mechanism that Bernard (1974a) considered to be the major sorting mechanism in filter-feeding bivalves.

Thus, according to the conventional mucociliary concept of filter feeding in bivalves, inertial forces are active from the moment the ambient water enters the mantle cavity until it passes through the interfilament canals, deplet-

[*11*]

ed of particles. It may therefore be of interest to assess the relative importance of viscous and inertial forces in determining the path of a suspended
particle in the flow passing through a filter-feeding bivalve.

Bernard (1974a) calculated settling velocities of various-sized particles
of a density of 2.5, based on Stokes equation for drag of a sphere $D = 6\pi\eta av$,
where η is the viscosity, a is the radius and v is the velocity. These settling
velocities were compared with flow velocities of the through current at the
level of the entrance to the interfilament canals, estimated to be about
0.3 mm s^{-1}, and he calculated that particles larger than about 14 μm would
settle without reaching the gills. The relevant parameter, however, is not the
flow velocity at the gill surface but the time it takes the water to reach the
gills and to pass through the bivalve. In the 8 cm oyster (*Crassostrea gigas*)
on which Bernard based his calculations, the transit time of the through current can be estimated to be in the order of 10 s, corresponding to a mean
velocity of 1 cm s^{-1}. The settling velocity of a 14 μm particle is about 0.3
mm s^{-1}, and of a 50 μm particle about 2 mm s^{-1}, or an order of magnitude
smaller than the mean velocity of the through current. Settling of large particles cannot therefore prevent mineral particles from reaching and 'imping-
ing' upon the 'delicate' gill tissue, as Bernard assumed.

Impingement of heavy particles on the surface of the gill filaments depends upon the inertial momentum of the particles in the laminar flow directed towards the surface of the gill. This momentum will cause particles
directed towards the frontal surface of the filaments to deviate from the
streamlines when the through current is deflected to pass between the
filaments. The distance, d, from the streamline towards the filament, which
the momentum will take a particle, can be calculated from $d = 0.5\pi r v_p/v_0$,
where r is the radius of a circular path, v_0 is the tangential velocity component and v_p is the perpendicular component, due to inertial forces (Fenchel,
1980). In the calculations r is assumed to be 35 μm, corresponding to the
distance between the midline of the frontal surface of the filament and the
flow through a neighbouring interfilament canal (Figure 6), and v_0 is assumed to be 0.1 cm s^{-1} (Jørgensen *et al.*, 1986b). v_p can be calculated from
the equation $v_p = d^2(\rho_p - \rho_f)v_0^2/18\,r\eta$, where d is the diameter of the particle,
ρ_p and ρ_f are the densities of particle and fluid, respectively, and η is the viscosity (Fenchel, 1980). A circular path with a radius of 35 μm presumably
represents an extreme curvature of the streamlines of the through currents.
The calculated deviations of particle pathways due to the centrifugal force

[12]

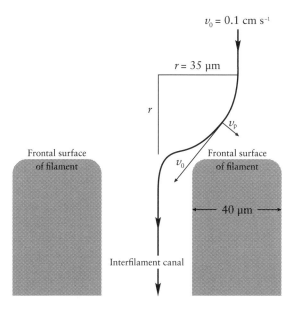

Figure 6. Acceleration of a particle along a deflected streamline in the currents passing between the gill filaments in a filter-feeding bivalve, r is radius of deflection curvature, v_0 is the tangential velocity component and v_p is the perpendicular component due to inertial forces.

thus seem to be upper estimates. The departure of the 14 μm particle from its streamline amounted to $4.3 \cdot 10^{-2}$ μm, or 0.3% of the particle diameter. For the 50 μm particle the corresponding value was 0.54 μm, or about 1.1% of the particle diameter. Inertial forces thus exert insignificant effects on the path of even large and heavy particles heading with the current towards the gill surface, the viscous forces preventing any physical contact between particles and surfaces by way of impingement.

Finally, it seems doubtful whether particles come into direct contact with the laterofrontal cirri as part of the capture mechanism, and captured particles do not necessarily make contact with the cilia of the frontal tracts (see Chapter VII).

CHAPTER III

Observation of undisturbed feeding

Usually it is understood, often implicitly, that observations made on preparations also apply in the intact, undisturbed animal. MacGinitie (1941) questioned this, and he attempted to observe feeding in undisturbed bivalves through a glass window covering a hole drilled in a valve and cut through the underlying mantle. MacGinitie found that the operation resulted in abnormal feeding, and it took some weeks in fresh sea water before the operated bivalves resumed normal feeding. During this a mucus sheet was assumed to cover the frontal surface of the gill, acting as a filter to strain particles from the through current. MacGinitie did not actually observe the mucus sheet, mucus being invisible, but he inferred its presence from the observation that particles retained on the gill surface in undisturbed bivalves changed their course from one that closely followed the frontal ciliary tracts to one that crossed the gill filaments, independently of existing ciliary tracts.

Foster-Smith (1975, 1978) resumed observations of feeding in bivalves furnished with windows. The animals, *Mytilus edulis*, *Cerastoderma edule* and *Venerupis pullastra*, were kept in running sea water where they might remain healthy for many months. The experimental conditions therefore seemed compatible with normal feeding. Foster-Smith did, however, not observe mucus sheets but mucus strings extending across the gill filaments. Algal cells used as food were observed embedded in the mucus strings, whereas single cells were rarely seen even at low concentrations. Foster-Smith was thus unable to confirm the filtering mechanism proposed by MacGinitie, but agreed with the final result that captured food particles are embedded in mucus.

Bernard (1974a) made an extensive study of the feeding processes in the Pacific oyster *Crassostrea gigas*. Movements of particles, colloidal graphite and sand grains, on the gills of undisturbed oysters were recorded and measured after careful removal of the anterior portion of a valve. Animals survived several months after the operation and appeared to function normally. This function varied with the concentration of suspended particles. At low

[*14*]

concentrations the frontal surface of the gill filaments is stated to be covered by bands of a serous mucus that entraps prospective food particles. At high concentrations another type of mucus, produced by the goblet cells, was secreted to entangle particles destined for rejection. Bernard's observations are discussed below (p. 28). Presently, it can be concluded that available reports on the function of the gills in supposedly undisturbed feeding bivalves are difficult to reconcile. However, the descriptions agree in food particles being entrapped in mucus on the gill surface. The descriptions are thus in accordance with the traditional mucociliary concept of the feeding mechanism.

CHAPTER IV

Ciliary filter feeding without mucus

Transport of particles in water currents along the surface of the bivalve gill or along other ciliated tracts has been described repeatedly over the years (e.g., Bronn, 1862; Stenta, 1903; Segerdahl, 1922; Gray, 1929; Nicol, 1931; Gosselin & O'Hara, 1961; Strathmann & Leise, 1977; Gilmour, 1979). Any observer of veliger larvae in a fresh sample of zooplankton will be familiar with the free rotation and intermingling of particles within the stomach, witnessing the absence of mucus from ingested food particles. Accordingly, feeding in veligers and other ciliary-feeding planktonic larvae has been described without involving mucus as part of the feeding mechanism (Fretter & Montgommery, 1968; Millar, 1955; Strathmann *et al.*, 1972; Thompson, 1959). Yonge (1926-1927), however, does state that veligers embed food particles in mucus.

Descriptions of transport of food particles in suspension in currents produced by ciliary tracts usually pass without comment, presumably because of unawareness of any problem being inherent in such transport. To those who did recognize a problem, mucus secreted by the ciliated epithelium was the only means of preventing captured particles from escaping the ciliary tracts which transport the particles to the mouth. A tacit awareness of the problem presumably lay behind Yonge's (1947) statement that the gill fila-

[15]

ments cannot function until the all-important food groove along the ventral margin of a demibranch is complete. This assertion Stasek (1962) found to be unwarranted, as ciliary currents along the free margins of the developing demibranchs were seen to carry particles towards the mouth before the food groove had begun to differentiate. Yonge (1935) also dismissed Nicol's (1931) conclusion that mucus plays little, if any, part in the feeding process in the polychaete *Sabella pavonina*, and Morton (1967) probably expressed a general feeling by stating that unbound with mucus 'a multitude of small unruly particles would be no sooner collected than dispersed'.

This persistence on mucus being needed to keep collected particles on the ciliary tracts is remarkable in view of the easy demonstration that it is not (Fretter & Montgommery, 1968; Jørgensen, 1975a, 1976a, 1981a; Owen, 1974b; Owen & McCrae, 1976). Thus, if gills or gill fragments of a bivalve are exposed to a suspension of particles, such as cultured flagellates, it can be observed that the flagellates are collected and concentrated in water currents along gill filaments and dorsal or ventral food grooves. As long as the flagellates move suspended in the surface currents, their own movements do not suffice to help them escape from the currents. However, at the cut ends of a tract, where the flow of water stops, concentrated suspensions of flagellates immediately redisperse in the ambient water. Redispersed flagellates do not tend to adhere to each other, and they continue to swim normally, indicating that they have not become smeared with mucus during the process of retention and transport by the gill. Flagellates and other particles that do become entangled in mucus accumulate at cut ends of ciliary tracts without being resuspended in the water (Jørgensen, 1976a).

Forces must therefore act upon the particles to keep them in suspension within the water currents produced by the ciliary tracts. Jørgensen (1981a) suggested that these forces are the same as those that maintain particles moving in laminar flow along a wall at a certain distance from the wall (Cox & Hsu, 1977; Leal, 1980). Fluid mechanical forces acting on particles suspended in laminar ciliary currents thus constitute an alternative mechanism for the entrapping of particles, besides the entrapment in mucus transported directly by ciliary action.

The transport of particles in suspension in the food grooves is difficult to reconcile with the descriptions of feeding in presumably undisturbed bivalves, as observed through a window in a valve. It is therefore crucial to know in what state the food arrives in the stomach.

[16]

An extensive literature deals with the stomach content of filter-feeding bivalves and with the ways the stomach deals with ingested food. This literature consistently refers to food as particles embedded in mucus (e.g., Bernard, 1974a; Kristensen, 1972; List, 1902; Morton, 1960; Reid, 1965; Vonk, 1924; Yonge, 1935). Ingestion of particles in mucus has also been directly observed. Thus, Allen (1958) recorded that most of the material accepted after sorting on the labial palps entered the oesophagus within a string of mucus that was subsequently wrapped around the tip of the crystalline style. Churchill & Lewis (1924) fed young transparent stages of many species of freshwater bivalves with suspensions of bottom material, carmine particles, etc., and they observed that particles intercepted by the gills were entangled in mucus and carried to the labial palps for ingestion or rejection.

Allen's (1958) observations were made on preparations and those of Churchill & Lewis (1924) with thick suspensions. The observations may therefore not refer to normal feeding. In case of stomach analysis, it cannot be excluded that the filling of the stomach with mucus may result from the mutilation involved in the opening of the animal, which strongly stimulates mucus secretion. In intact mussels clearing suspensions of graphite, samples of the stomach content were therefore taken by pipette immediately after cutting of the adductor muscle (Jørgensen, 1981b). The composition of the stomach content is shown in Table 1. In five out of eight mussels practically all graphite ingested was present in a freely suspended state. Some stomach samples contained varying amounts of particles embedded in mucus besides particles in suspension. Particles retained by the gills are thus predominantly ingested in the suspended state. Moreover, ingestion of particles can occur simultaneously with the elimination of mucus-embedded particles as pseudofaeces. Table 1 shows that under similar conditions the behaviour of mus-

Table 1. *Mytilus edulis*. State of stomach content in 12 intact mussels clearing suspensions of graphite particles (from Jørgensen, 1981b)

	Stomach content		
	suspended	suspended or mucus-embedded	absent
Pseudofaeces not produced	2	2	0
Pseudofaeces produced	3	1	4

[17]

Right inner labial palp   Left outer labial palp

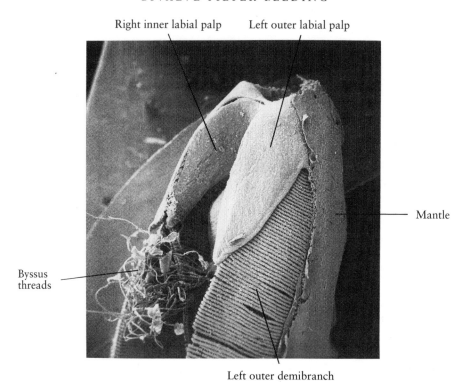

Mantle

Byssus
threads

Left outer demibranch

Figure 7. *Mytilus edulis*. Scanning electron micrograph of a small, rapidly frozen mussel, showing position of labial palps characteristic for normal feeding. The mussel was removed from the valves after freeze-drying (from Jørgensen, 1981b).

sels might vary from ingestion of all retained particles in suspension to complete rejection of particles as pseudofaeces. Also Kiørboe & Møhlenberg (1981) found that algal food particles, *Phaeodactylum tricornutum*, fed to mussels below and above the threshold for pseudofaeces production, were freely suspended in samples of the oesophagus content, taken within 30 seconds of opening of the mussels.

Apparently, something happens to the feeding mechanism shortly after opening of the mussels, which could be verified by direct observation (Jørgensen, 1981b). Immediately after exposure of the mantle cavity the labial palps mostly occupied the position shown in Figure 7. Each pair of palps enclosed the anterior marginal portions of an outer and inner demibranch, and the lips were closed. This seems to represent the position of the

[*18*]

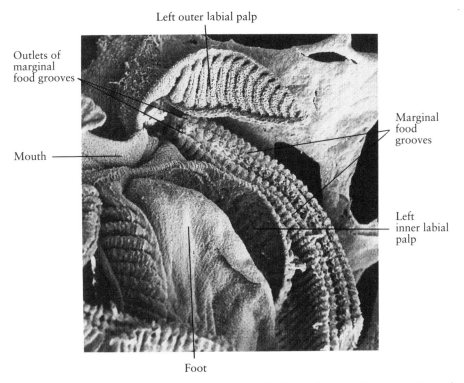

Figure 8. *Mytilus edulis*. Scanning electron micrograph of a small mussel showing position of lips and labial palps characteristic of disturbed mussels. The antero-ventral parts of the demi-branchs have become exposed (from Jørgensen, 1981b).

labial palps in bivalves exhibiting undisturbed feeding (Bernard, 1974a; MacGinitie, 1941; Yonge, 1926-27).

Within seconds after cutting of the adductor muscle the palps began to move away from the gills, and after about a minute they usually occupied positions similar to those shown in Figure 8. The palps and lips are spread wide apart, and they expose the ventral margins of the gills and their relation to the mouth. It seems of special importance that the marginal food grooves of the demibranchs terminate close to the corners of the mouth.

Within a minute after cutting of the adductor muscle in mussels that had been filtering graphite suspension, thin black strings of mucus-embedded graphite particles could be seen to pass from the outlets of the marginal food grooves to the corners of the mouth and down the oesophagus. The mucus

[19]

strings rapidly grew in thickness. Thick strings of mucus, spanning across the filaments of large parts of the gill, were carried down the gill surface to be transported outside the food grooves along the free margins of the demi-branchs. To begin with these bulk masses of mucus passed down the oesoph-agus, but ingestion soon stopped and mucus that continued to be carried along the demibranch margins to the mouth region passed on to the palps. These observations thus indicate that mucus found in the stomach of mus-sels has arrived there secondarily, as a result of the mutilation prior to in-vestigations of the stomach content.

CHAPTER V

Mucus and sorting of particles: cleaning and feeding

The suspensions to which filter-feeding bivalves are exposed in nature are mixtures of particles of food value, particularly phytoplankton, and par-ticles without food value, particularly silt, usually present at concentrations that are many times higher than those of food particles. High concentrations of silt reduce the overall food value of the suspended particulate matter by a dilution effect. Above threshold concentrations for the production of pseu-dofaeces this dilution effect would be counterbalanced if mechanisms exist-ed by which the bivalves were able to sort food particles from silt for pref-erential ingestion of food. Such sorting has been demonstrated in a number of filter-feeding bivalves (Kiørboe & Møhlenberg, 1981; Kiørboe *et al.*, 1980; Newell & Jordan, 1983). However, the efficiency of selection varied greatly between species.

Kiørboe & Møhlenberg (1981) determined the efficiency with which ten species of filter-feeding bivalves separated algae from silt presented as a sus-pension of $10\text{-}30 \cdot 10^3$ cells ml^{-1} and 10-20 mg l^{-1} of bottom material. The selection efficiency was expressed as the ratio of the chlorophyll *a* (mg dry wt)$^{-1}$ in the suspension offered and in the pseudofaeces rejected by the undisturbed filtering bivalves. This ratio varied from 2.3 in *Arctica islandica* to 15.8 in *Spisula subtruncata*. The efficiency with which the bivalves sorted

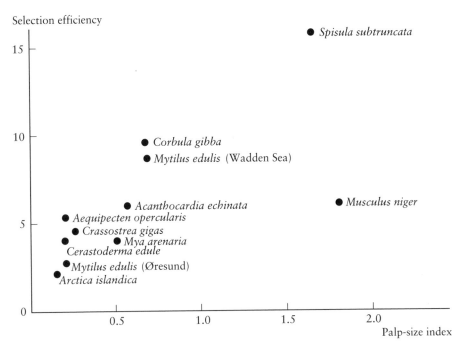

Figure 9. Plot of selection efficiency (relative chlorophyl *a* concentration in inhalant water/relative chlorophyl *a* concentration in pseudofaeces) against palp-size index (palp area relative to clearance) in bivalves filtering a mixture of algae and silt (from Kiørboe & Møhlenberg, 1981).

algae from silt was highly correlated with the size of the labial palps, expressed by the ratio palp area (mm^2)/clearance (ml min^{-1}) (Figure 9).

The efficiency of selection could not be related to gill type, and there was no clear correlation between selection efficiency or palp size and the turbidity of the species habitat. However, such correlation was striking in the two mussel populations investigated (Figure 9). The Wadden Sea mussels, which are exposed to concentrations up to several hundreds of mg l^{-1}, have larger labial palps and more efficient particle selection than the mussels from Øresund, where the maximum concentration of particulate matter recorded in bottom-near water is about 10 mg l^{-1} (Kiørboe & Møhlenberg, 1981; Theisen, 1982).

Selection among particles of food value, such as various types of algae, has also been reported. Thus Shumway *et al.* (1985) investigated selection of algae in mixtures of the dinoflagellate *Prorocentrum minimum*, the diatom *Phaeodactylum tricornutum* and the flagellate *Chroomonas salina* in a

[21]

number of filter-feeding bivalves. From their results they concluded that selective mechanisms may be located both on the gills and palps, as well as in
the stomach. Selection on the gills was restricted to the European oyster,
Ostrea edulis, selection at this level being absent in the five remaining species
studied, including the American oyster, *Crassostrea virginica*. Selection on
the gills of *Ostrea edulis* was inferred from the finding that during the experiment, which lasted 1 h, the oysters preferentially cleared *Prorocentrum
minimum* cells. However, Table I in the article shows that the clearance of
the dinoflagellate was relatively high only during the first half hour of the
experiment. During the second half hour the dinoflagellate was cleared at a
lower rate than that of the two other algae. Moreover, in all experiments the
bivalves were clearing the water at low rates (Table IV in the article), corresponding to only 3-15 % of the capacity of the filter pump, as calculated
from the data given in Table 10 (p. 86), which describes the relationships
between body mass and rate of water processing in unrestrained bivalves.

In *Mytilus edulis*, Ward & Targett (1989) in some instances obtained
statistically significant preferential ingestion or rejection of microparticles
treated with algal filtrates, and they suggested that chemical cues from mi-
croalgae can influence the feeding behaviour of mussel. Notably, however,
selection was erratic and marginal, significant changes in proportions of test
particles in suspension and in faeces or pseudofaeces amounting to about 5%.

In the experiments of Kiørboe & Møhlenberg (1981) the bivalves were
filtering the ambient water at high, optimal rates, and there is thus clear evidence for sorting of food particles from silt. The close correlation between
palp size and selection efficiency suggested the labial palps to be the site of
sorting, but mechanisms remained obscure.

If sorting of particles for acceptance or rejection does occur on the labial
palps the sorting mechanism presumably must be operating within a matrix
of mucus, entangling the particles. This is because only the mucus-embedded material that travels along the ventral margin of the demibranchs outside the food groove seems to be transferred onto the palps where these en-
close the margins of the demibranchs (Figure 7). Particulate matter in suspension is transported inside the food groove directly to the mouth. No
tracts are known to lead from the food grooves onto the palps. Ciliary currents on the palp surface are capable of separating smaller fragments or even
single particles or cells from larger masses of mucus-embedded material.
The separation of single particles from the main mass does, however, not

[22]

free the particles of mucus. This can be inferred from the stickiness the particles have acquired. Even strong mechanical treatment of mucus-bound particles, such as repeated sucking up of pseudofaeces into a pipette followed by forceful ejection of the material, did not remove the stickiness from separated individual particles or cells (own unpublished observations).

Newell & Jordan (1983) attempted to explain sorting of particles on the labial palps by suggesting that the mucus passing between the opposing palps changes from a mucous to a serous state, by which change the particles should become free to move and thus accessible for sorting. Mucus may in fact change its rheological properties when exposed to shearing stress. Mucus is secreted as a viscoelastic substance, a property of fundamental importance for its function in clearing ciliated surfaces (Litt, 1971). At high shear rates mucus looses its elastic properties with a concurrent decrease in viscosity, and it assumes Newtonian properties (Denny & Gosline, 1980; Grenon & Walker, 1980; Reid, 1970; Ronkin, 1955; Simkiss & Wilbur, 1977). It has been hypothesized that shearing stress may be responsible, at least partially, for the establishment of serous sublayers surrounding the cilia in mucociliary systems, which are of widespread occurrence among animals (Blake, 1973; Blake & Sleigh, 1974; Simkiss & Wilbur, 1977). However, if ciliary tracts do exert shear forces high enough to affect the rheological properties of mucus, such effects seem to be restricted to the ciliary sublayer, and not to extend beyond the ciliary tips (Blake, 1973), that is, to the level of a possible sorting. It therefore seems unlikely that mechanisms exist on the palps that can re-establish conditions compatible with sorting of individual particles.

The lack of sorting of particles in suspension on the palps is further supported by Kiørboe et al.'s (1980) finding of a threshold value for the addition of silt before the selection mechanism becomes operative and pseudofaeces production starts. In *Mytilus edulis* this threshold was 1 mg silt l^{-1}. If exposure of mixtures of algae and silt in suspension to sorting mechanisms on the palps is obligatory, it is difficult to understand how such sorting can remain inoperative below certain concentrations of silt. Kiørboe et al. also found a linear relationship between the rate of production of pseudofaeces and the material retained by the gills. As the rate at which the material was retained increased from 0.057 mg min^{-1} to about 3 mg min^{-1}, pseudofaeces production increased from zero to close to 3 mg min^{-1}, corresponding to only a moderate increase in ingestion rate from about 32 µg min^{-1} at a silt

[23]

concentration of 1 mg l^{-1} to 50 μg min^{-1} at a 60 times higher concentration of silt. Such a regulation of the ingestion rate concurrently with the rejection of increasing proportions of retained material after sorting is consistent with the concept of a restricted capacity of the food grooves for transporting particles in suspension, any surplus being taken care of by mucus produced by the gills and eventually transferred to the labial palps. This would imply a re-location of the sorting from the palps to the gills.

Sorting of particles presumably depends upon the ability simultaneously to ingest particles in suspension and to eliminate mucus-bound particles as pseudofaeces. This ability again depends upon spatial separation of acceptance and rejection tracts on the gills. How such separation ensues may be elucidated by observations of the exposed gill surface in, e.g., *Mytilus edulis* (Jørgensen, 1981b).

As mentioned, cutting of the adductor muscle to expose the gill surface strongly stimulated the secretion of mucus, but the secretion gradually abated to reach low levels within some hours. The secretion did not, however, stop as in the intact mussel not producing pseudofaeces. The mussels with cut adductor muscle responded with profuse secretion of mucus to low concentrations of particles in the water. Mutilation of mussels thus enhanced the sensitivity of the mechanism that controls the secretion of mucus in response to particulate matter in the water passing through the gill. However, the close relationship persisted between the concentration of particulate matter and the rate of secretion of mucus.

It is not well understood how the concentration of particles controls the rate of mucus secretion. Presumably, the mechanism is based on physical stimuli since chemically inert particles, such as graphite particles, are equally efficient in stimulating mucus secretion as are algal or yeast cells. As particles suspended in the through current do not make physical contact with the gill filaments, we should look for physical stimuli that are active at a distance from the filament surface. The forces involved may be the same as the fluid mechanical forces that keep suspended particles within the surface currents at a distance from the surface. These forces act between the particles and the filament surface. The magnitude of the integrated force must vary with the concentration and size of particles suspended in the water currents along the filament surfaces. If mucus secretion is, in fact, stimulated by these forces the ensuing secretion should vary with concentration and size of particles suspended in the ambient water, consistent with observation.

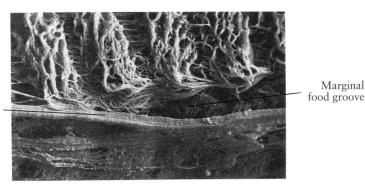

Bundle of
mucus threads
containing
scattered
particles

Marginal
food groove

Figure 10. *Mytilus edulis*. Scanning electron micrograph of margin of an excised gill, showing accumulation of mucus threads along the outer marginal ciliary tract (from Jørgensen, 1981b).

Mucus secreted forms tiny threads that tend to coalesce into longer and longer threads or strings traversing many filaments (Figure 10). These mucus strings are carried directly on the ciliary tracts and they advance slowly compared with the water currents that flow over the strings. Particles suspended in the currents along the frontal surface of the filaments thus pass the mucus strings at close distance and may even make contact with and stick to the mucus, that is, pass from an ingestion pathway to a rejection pathway. The chance of being caught in a mucus string must depend upon the rate of secretion of mucus, which determines the thickness and spacing of the mucus strings traversing the filaments. Presumably, capture of particles by the mucus also depends upon size, shape and surface properties of the particles. The spatial and temporal relationships between the surface currents along the gill filaments and the mucus strings carried across the filaments thus seem to provide a basis for the selective rejection of particles from mixtures when the total concentration of particulate matter in suspension exceeds the capacity of the digestive tract.

The mechanism here proposed suggests that with increasing rates of mucus secretion, i.e., particle concentration, the chances for the particles to be caught in a mucus string also increase, so that eventually the total number of particles reaching the mouth may decrease despite increasing particle concentrations in the ambient water. As shown by Kiørboe *et al.* (1980) this concentration may be high, in mussels exceeding 50 mg l^{-1} of silt.

The hypothesis outlined for the mechanism of particle sorting (Jørgensen 1981b, 1990a) is based primarily on observations of the filibranch gill

[25]

of mussels, but presumably it applies equally well to plicate gills which exhibit a more pronounced spatial separation of rejection tracts and acceptance tracts. The ciliary tracts on the plical crests transport mucus strings that may span across several plicae (Foster-Smith, 1975). In most species this transport is ventral to the margin and further along to the labial palps. Simultaneously, suspended particles are carried in currents, created along the filaments that constitute the troughs of the plicae, to the currents within the dorsal and/or ventral food grooves leading directly to the mouth (Figure 1, p. 6). As mentioned, there was nothing, though, to indicate that plicate gills were correlated with more efficient separation of algae from silt (Kiørboe & Møhlenberg, 1981).

If the complex system of folds and ciliary tracts on the inside of the palps does not act to sort particles the function remains to be ascertained. This may be to shape the particle-loaded mucus strings into pseudofaeces. Observations of exposed palps in preparations of mussels with cut adductor muscle show that the activity of the ciliary tracts tends to rotate and wind up mucus strings. This winding-up presumably constitutes the major feature in the formation of pseudofaeces before they are dropped onto rejection tracts along the mantle edges. Such a function of the palps in the formation of pseudofaeces would be consistent with the finding that *Mytilus edulis* from habitats characterized by high particle loads, correlated with high levels of pseudofaeces formation, also possess larger palps than do mussels from populations exposed to only low particle loads (Kiørboe & Møhlenberg, 1981; Theisen, 1982).

CHAPTER VI

Reconciliation of views

As mentioned, it has repeatedly been realized that the ciliary tracts on the surface of the bivalve gill produce water currents, as do ciliated surfaces generally. Bronn (1862) stated that water currents along the frontal surface of the gill filaments carried particles retained by the gill filter to the ventral margin of the demibranchs where the particles passed forward towards the mouth in water currents within the food groove. However, Bronn did not distinguish between particles in suspension and bound in mucus, which he described as being added during the passage of food particles, so that at the level of the mouth it was a mucus string loaded with particles that was carried in a water current. At the turn of the century the ambiguity in concepts of particle transport along the gill filaments and marginal food groove was resolved in the statement that retained particles are bound to mucus strings that are transported by physical contact with the beating cilia (Stenta, 1903; Wallengren, 1905b). After mucus had been generally accepted as an integral element in the feeding process, descriptions often omitted mentioning its presence, and its involvement in the treatment of particles on gills and palps can only be inferred, e.g., from a casual reference to the production of pseudofaeces (Stasek, 1965). The vast amount of observations published on particle transport and sorting on the various types of bivalve gills seems, however, to fit the concept of two distinct mechanisms of ciliary particle transport: particles may be carried along ciliary tracts free in suspension within the laminar currents produced by the ciliary tracts or bound to mucus that tends to be transported by direct ciliary contact.

This distinction between two separate physical states for particle transport along gill filaments may also resolve the widely accepted paradox that tracts of fine cilia selectively transport small and light particles and that tracts of coarse cilia selectively transport large and heavy particles. There seems to be no physical basis for a preference of 'fine' cilia for small particles and of 'coarse' cilia for large particles. Moreover, the distinction between 'fine' and 'coarse' cilia is misleading because the diameter of cilia forming the fine and coarse ciliary tracts is the same, viz. 0.2 μm, the standard diameter of cilia and flagella. But the cilia are sparsely and evenly distributed along the lateral 'fine' tracts as compared with the median 'coarse' tract, where the densely spaced cilia tend to form cirral-like tufts (Owen & McCrae, 1976; Ribelin & Collier, 1977).

The interpretations in terms of particle selection by means of 'fine' and 'coarse' ciliary tracts are based on observations made on exposed gills under conditions where mucus is produced and rejection tracts thus activated. Under such conditions we now know that the gill surface presents two different environments to particles, laminar surface currents along the filaments and mucus strings passing perpendicularly to these currents. Median frontal ciliary tracts on the gill surface constitute prominences, both on fili-branch gills and on plicate gills where the dense tracts are preferentially found on the crests. These structural features result in the mucus strings primarily being formed and transported by the activity of the tracts of 'coarse' cilia. Given that large particles in suspension in the surface currents are more likely to be caught than small particles when the particles pass a mucus string, the overall pattern of events appears to be that large particles are preferentially transported by tracts of 'coarse' cilia and small particles by tracts of 'fine' cilia.

Finally, an attempt should be made to reconcile Bernard's (1974a) description of feeding in *Crassostrea gigas* with that presented here. As mentioned, Bernard states that prospective food particles are entrapped in watery, serous mucus overlying the frontal cilia. The thickness of the layer is given as 17 μm, or about three times the length of the frontal cilia. This feeding mucus is stated to constitute a continuous stream moving from the gills towards the mouth whether food particles are present or not. From the dimension of the stream and its travelling speed Bernard calculated that the rate of mucus production in an 8.2 cm long oyster would amount to 7.9 cm^3 h^{-1}. He also obtained mucus from the food grooves and at the mouth by dissection of oysters fed algae and rapid sampling of the mucus with a micropipette. He made the important observation that the mucus from the food grooves contained on average 3.1 % of dry material against 12 % in the mucus from the mouth region. According to Bernard this concentration of matter takes place on the palps, which reduce the mucus so that the particles enter the mouth in one fourth the original volume.

At a rate of secretion of 7.9 ml of mucus per h containing 3.1 % of dry algal matter, $7.9 \cdot 0.031 = 0.24$ g algal matter would be ingested per h. It is not stated at which concentration of algae the oysters were fed, but since they did not secrete 'rejection' mucus the concentration was below the threshold for the production of pseudofaeces, that is, about 1 mg l^{-1} of suspended matter. Neither is it stated at what rate the oysters cleared the water. If we assume a filtration rate of 7 l h^{-1} (Table 10, p. 86) and a food concentration of 1 mg l^{-1}, in the absence of pseudofaeces formation this corresponds to an ingestion rate of 7 mg h^{-1}, or $(7/240) \cdot 100 = 3$ % of the rate calculated by Bernard. This would imply that the mucus flow in the food grooves amounts to only a small fraction of the flow that transports the food particles along the frontal surface of the gill filaments. Such a reduction in

[28]

volume of secreted mucus at the transition from the filaments to the marginal food groove is not easily explained. But there are reasons to believe that Bernard's statements concerning the secretion of serous mucus along the frontal filaments for the confinement of food particles may constitute an interpretation of observations felt to imply such secretion. It thus seems that the observations and data available are consistent with the fluid mechanical mechanism for the transport of particles suggested above. This mechanism implies stepwise and steep increases in concentration of suspended particles at the transition from the surface currents along the gill filaments to the marginal food grooves and again from these grooves to the oesophagus, the increases in concentration corresponding to the reductions in volume of the currents containing the particles (Jørgensen, 1981b).

CHAPTER VII

Mechanism of particle retention

The laterofrontal cirri have played a dominant role in the literature on the function of the bivalve gill in feeding. The position of the cirri along the edges of the frontal surface of the filaments, where they bridge the entrance to the interfilament canals, as well as their beat towards the frontal ciliary tract, quite naturally led to the view that the laterofrontal cirri act as sieves. As mentioned, the cirri have generally been stated to filter the passing water and to throw intercepted particles onto the frontal ciliary tract (Wallengren, 1905b; Orton, 1912; Yonge, 1926-27; Atkins, 1937a,b, 1938; Clausen, 1958; Dral, 1967; Morton, 1969, 1983). The function as filters was considered finally established when scanning electron microscopy showed the tips of the individual cilia to branch off from the cirral shaft to form a strikingly filter-like structure (Hughes, 1975; Moore, 1971; Owen, 1974a; Ribelin & Collier, 1977) (Figure 11).

If the laterofrontal cirri do, in fact, act as mechanical sieves in retaining particles suspended in the through current, the efficiencies with which the gills retain particles of various sizes should be determined by the distances

[29]

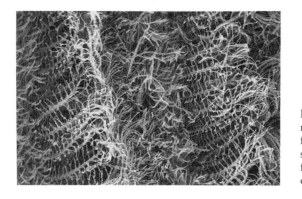

Figure 11. *Mytilus edulis*. Scanning electron micrograph of frontal surface of gill filaments, showing the branching laterofrontal cirri (Michael Nemanic, original).

Efficiency of retention, %

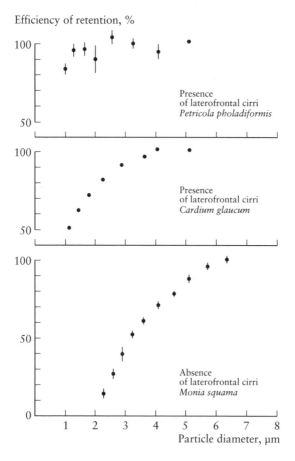

Presence
of laterofrontal cirri
Petricola pholadiformis

Presence
of laterofrontal cirri
Cardium glaucum

Absence
of laterofrontal cirri
Monia squama

Particle diameter, μm

Figure 12. Examples of the relation between efficiency of particle retention and presence or absence of laterofrontal cirri in filter-feeding bivalves (from Jørgensen *et al.*, 1984).

[30]

between the side branches of the cirri. In *Mytilus edulis* this distance is about 1 μm which should accordingly constitute the smallest size of particles that do not pass the filter (Jørgensen, 1975a). But the gills start to become leaky at a particle size of about 3-4 μm, not only in *Mytilus*, but also in several other bivalves that possess well developed laterofrontal cirri (Jørgensen, 1975a; Jørgensen *et al.*, 1984; Lucas *et al.*, 1987; Møhlenberg & Riisgård, 1978; Riisgård, 1988a; Vahl, 1972a, 1973a). Moreover, filter-feeding bivalves with short (oysters) or undeveloped (scallops, anomiids) laterofrontal cirri do also efficiently retain small particles (Haven & Morales-Alamo, 1970; Jørgensen & Goldberg, 1953; Møhlenberg & Riisgård, 1978; Riisgård, 1988a; Vahl, 1972a,b, 1973a,b). In these microciliobranchiate bi-

Table 2. Efficiency of particle retention in relation to development of the laterofrontal cirri in marine filter-feeding bivalves (data from Møhlenberg & Riisgård, 1978; Jørgensen *et al.*, 1984; Riisgård, 1988a)

Species	Particle diameters, μm	
	90% retention	50% retention
Laterofrontal cirri well developed		
Cardium glaucum	3	1
C. echinatum	2	1
C. (Cerastoderma) edule	2	1.5
Mytilus edulis	3	1
Modiolus modiolus	2.5	1
Musculus niger	2.5	1
Geukensia (Modiolus) demissa	3	≈1
Cultellus pellucidus	3	1
Hiatella striata	2.5	<1
Mya arenaria	3	1.5
Arctica islandica	2	<1
Venerupis pullastra	2.5	1
Brachidontes exustus	3.5	2.5
Spisula solidissima	3.5	2
Mercenaria mercenaria	3.5	2
Laterofrontal cirri small or lacking		
Ostrea edulis	4.5	2
Crassostrea virginica	5	2.5
Pecten opercularis	5.5	4
P. septemradiatus	5.5	4
Argopecten irradians	4	2.5
Monia squama	5	3

[31]

valves (Atkins, 1938), the threshold sizes for complete retention of particles are, however, somewhat higher than in bivalves with well developed cirri, viz. about 5-6 μm in *Crassostrea virginica*; *Pecten* spp. and *Monia squama* (Jørgensen *et al.*, 1984; Møhlenberg & Riisgård, 1978; Riisgård, 1988a) (Figure 12 and Table 2).

Particles can thus be transferred from the through currents into the surface currents running along the gill filaments in the absence of a mechanical filtering device. We should therefore look for other filtering principles. In order to explain particle capture in bivalves possessing plicate gills, Owen & McCrae (1976) suggested that a region of low pressure created within the interplicate grooves tends to attract particles, but the physical forces acting are not clear. Jørgensen (1975a, 1976a) speculated that particle capture by the bivalve gills depends upon the functional integration of the different ciliary tracts on the frontal and lateral surfaces of the filaments. These tracts establish complex three-dimensional current patterns at the entrance to the interfilament canals. At this level, particles suspended in the ambient water are exposed to shear forces arising at the interfaces of the laminar currents. It was hypothesized that these shear forces were responsible for the transfer of suspended particles from the through current into the currents along the frontal surface of the filaments, i.e., capture of the particles (Jørgensen, 1981a).

In the first outline of the hypothesis it was suggested that the steady component of the interfilament currents and the surface currents were primarily responsible for the particle capture. Calculations showed, however, that this simple model could not explain the efficiency with which small suspended particles are transferred from the through current to the surface currents (Poul S. Larsen, cit. Jørgensen, 1982; Silvester & Sleigh, 1984). It was consequently suggested that the oscillatory currents produced by the band of lateral cilia at the entrance to the interfilament canals may play an important role in the mechanism of particle retention in the bivalve gill (Figure 13), but experimental and theoretical investigations are needed to evaluate the capacities and relative importance of the various components of the interfilament currents and surface currents in the capture of suspended particles (Jørgensen, 1983a).

The bivalve gill captures suspended particles on the upstream side of the pump proper, whereas particles are captured downstream by the velum of the larvae of bivalves and other molluscs (Jørgensen, 1989; Jørgensen *et al.*,

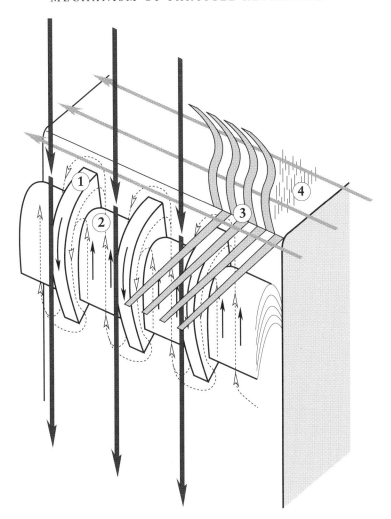

Figure 13. Spatial diagram of gill filament showing ciliary tracts and water currents. (1) Phase of effective stroke of metachronal wave of band of lateral cilia; (2) phase of recovery stroke of the wave; (3) tract of laterofrontal cirri alternatingly shown during resting phase crossing the interfilament canal, and at the end of the effective stroke normal to the frontal surface of the filament; (4) band of frontal cilia. Heavy arrows: ➤ indicate interfilament through current; ➤ indicate current along frontal surface of the filament. Light arrows: ➤ indicate directions of movement of the surface enveloping the metachronally beating band of lateral cilia; ┄┄┄▷ indicate oscillating water currents produced by the metachronal wave, which moves toward the left (from Jørgensen, 1982).

1984). High-speed video microscopy of feeding in the larval stages of the clam *Mercenaria mercenaria* indicates that also in the larvae particles are captured by patterns of fluid flow and shear gradients within the sublayer of the band of velar cirri rather than by direct interception (Gallager, 1988). The capture mechanism in the filament crown of the polychaete *Sabella pavonina* may be similar to that in the veligers (H.U. Riisgård, personal communication).

Murakami (1989) described particle retention in the mussel gill in terms of a ciliary reversal hypothesis, proposed by Strathmann *et al.* (1972) to explain particle capture in upstream collecting systems. Thus, according to Murakami a particle that touches the lateral cilia will induce depolarization of the cells, causing reversal of the stroke which will push the particle backwards, to be trapped in the transport system of the frontal cilia via the action of the laterofrontal cirri. The hypothesis disregards, however, evidence for the location of the capture mechanism at the entrance to the interfilament canals, which would exclude any direct involvement of the lateral cilia in the capture mechanism. Moreover, particles introduced in the current systems established by the bands of lateral cilia do not interfere with the normal metachronal pattern of beating of the cilia (Jørgensen, 1982).

The question of the functional significance of the laterofrontal cirri in the bivalve gills still lacks a final answer. The answer depends upon how much of the through current passes between the ciliary side branches on the cirri and how much of the current bypasses the cirri. The relative importance of the intracirral and intercirral pathways depends upon the relative resistances these pathways offer to the water flow. It was therefore important to estimate these resistances.

The resistance Δp to intracirral flow could be calculated from the equation established by Tamada & Fujikawa (1957), based on the model of a plane row of equally spaced parallel cylinders of equal diameter,

$$\Delta p = \frac{8\pi\eta U_0}{b(1 - 2\ln\tau + 1/6\tau^2 - 1/144\tau^4)} \, ,$$

where η is the viscosity of the fluid, U_0 is the unrestricted flow velocity, b is the centre distance between neighbouring cylinders, $\tau = \pi d/b$, d being the diameter of the cylinders. When applied on undisturbed filtering *Mytilus edulis*, the equation indicated that the intracirral pathway represented a pressure drop of ≥ 1 mm H_2O. A similar calculation for *Geukensia demissa*

[34]

provided a pressure drop of ≥ 3 mm H_2O (Jørgensen, 1981a, 1983a). It was concluded that the resistances to water flow, as expressed in these pressure drops were so high that only little water passed through the cirri, which therefore did not act as filters. The magnitude of the resistance offered by the laterofrontal cirri was also experimentally approached, and no significant frictional resistance could be demonstrated, indicating a low intercirral resistance (Jørgensen *et al.*, 1986b, 1988, see also the section on the pump characteristics, p. 43). It thus seems that the laterofrontal cirri move rather than filter water, probably contributing to the current along the frontal surface of the filaments, as indicated in Figure 13 (Jørgensen, 1981a). This conclusion is supported by the finding that the active stroke of the cirri includes a component directed towards the free end of the filament, as indicated in Figure 13 (Jørgensen, 1975a). Such function has previously been ascribed to the cirri by Wallengren (1905a) and Gray (1928). According to Gray (1928, p. 145) the laterofrontal cirri 'act as vanes to deflect the wave currents from between the filaments on to the surface of the latter.'

CHAPTER VIII

Measuring pumping rates

The rates at which filter feeders process the ambient water can be determined directly or indirectly. Direct methods have been applied to species in which inhalant and exhalant currents can be easily separated. Often the two currents are separated mechanically and the exhalant water sampled and measured. In bivalves, such direct techniques have especially been used in oysters and mussels (Collier & Ray, 1948; Davenport & Woolmington, 1982; Davids, 1964; Drinnan, 1964; Famme *et al.*, 1986; Galtsoff, 1946; Hildreth, 1976; Loosanoff & Engle, 1947; Nelson, 1935; White, 1968).

The drawbacks of direct methods, implying the mechanical separation of inhalant and exhalant currents combined with the collection of exhaled water, are the great sensitivity of filter-feeding bivalves to mechanical disturbance and the difficulties in avoiding the establishment of pressure gradients

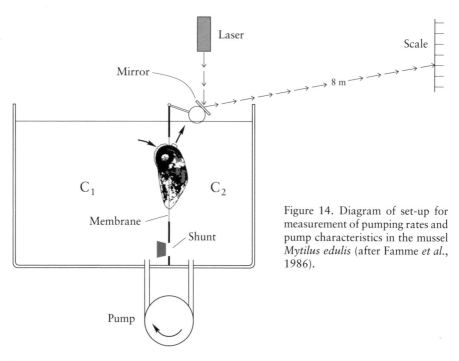

Figure 14. Diagram of set-up for measurement of pumping rates and pump characteristics in the mussel *Mytilus edulis* (after Famme *et al.*, 1986).

between inhalant and exhalant apertures. Pressure heads may arise in a set-up where the water pumped is collected via an overflow, where capillary forces may produce heads that interfere substantially with unrestrained pumping. Such error was avoided in the apparatus used by Famme *et al.* (1986). The apparatus was constructed specifically to determine the characteristics of the gill pump in the mussel *Mytilus edulis*, based on the relation between pumping rate and back pressure (see p. 44). The set-up is shown diagrammatically in Figure 14. A 5 litre aquarium was divided into two chambers (C_1 and C_2) by a silicone rubber membrane in which a slit had been cut. The mussel was inserted into the slit so that the membrane separated the inhalant current from the exhalant current. A shunt connected the two chambers when open. The water level in the exhalant chamber (C_2) was monitored with a laser beam striking a mirror that was fixed on a tethered floating ping-pong ball. The mirror reflected the laser beam onto a scale situated about 8 m from the mirror, a deflection of 1 cm on the scale corresponding to a 0.1 mm change in water level in C_2. When the mussel pumped water from C_1 to C_2 with the shunt closed, a pressure difference developed which could be fixed at any selected value by adjusting the calibrated peristaltic pump that pumped water back from C_2 to C_1.

Also flowmeters of various types that do not interfere mechanically with the animal have been used to record pumping rates (Amouroux et al, 1975; Coughlan & Ansell, 1964; McCammon, 1971; Reiswig, 1974; Sawyer, 1972; Wallengren, 1905a).

The indirect methods determine the volumes of water cleared of suspended particles per unit time. Particles may be algal cells, bacteria, inorganic and organic powders of various kinds, plastic spheres, etc. Clearances equal total amounts of water pumped, or filtration rates, when the suspended particles are totally retained by the filters.

Obviously, the indirect methods have wider applicability than direct methods. The volumes of water can be calculated from the exponential equation that relates changes in concentration of particles in a known volume of water with time: $C_t = C_0 e^{-mt/M}$, where C_t and C_0 are terminal and initial concentrations of particles, m is volume of water cleared, t is time and M is total volume. Volume cleared in unit time is clearance. Usually the equation is given on logarithmic form for the direct calculation of clearance $m = \ln(C_0/C_t) M/t$.

Clearance calculations were introduced almost simultaneously and independently to assess rates of water processing in copepods (Fuller, 1937; Harvey, 1937) and bivalves (Fox et al., 1937; Jørgensen, 1943). Coughlan (1969) reviewed the many ways in which different authors have used the exponential decline in particle concentration with time to calculate filtration rates.

In early investigations the media applied were enriched with suspended particles, such as graphite, clay or cultures of phytoplankton algae. Concentrations of particles were determined photometrically or by use of radioactively labelled cultures of algae (Chipman, 1959; Chipman & Hopkins, 1954; Jørgensen & Goldberg, 1953). The introduction of electronic particle counters greatly improved the indirect methods by permitting determinations to be made at natural concentrations of suspended particles in the water (Sheldon & Parsons, 1967). It thus became possible to measure the rates at which undisturbed suspension feeders clear the surrounding water of particles of various sizes under conditions that approach natural conditions.

It is a disadvantage of clearance measurements in the ordinary-type closed systems that the concentration of particles is declining during the experiment. The drawback was overcome in flow systems (Bayne et al. 1977;

[37]

Corner, 1961; Haven & Morales-Alamo, 1970; Hildreth & Crisp, 1976; Riisgård, 1977; Vahl, 1972a; Walne, 1972; Widdows & Bayne, 1971). The animals are kept in chambers through which the suspension flows at constant rates. The particle clearances can be calculated from the difference in particle concentrations in the water entering and leaving the chambers, and the flow rates of the water. In order to obtain clearance values that represent the total amount of suspension processed, shape and size of chambers and rates of water flow have to be chosen so as to prevent animals from recirculating the water in the chamber (Hildreth & Crisp, 1976; Riisgård, 1977).

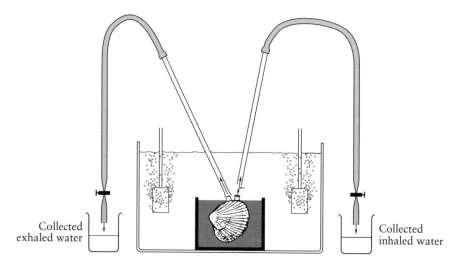

Collected
exhaled water

Collected
inhaled water

Figure 15. Diagram of set-up for measurement of rates of water processing (clearances) in filter-feeding bivalves. The glass tubes collect water from the inhalant and exhalant currents by gravity (from Møhlenberg & Riisgård, 1978).

Møhlenberg & Riisgård (1978, 1979) improved the indirect method of determining filtration rates by sampling inhaled and exhaled water through siphons placed above the inhalant and exhalant apertures of a bivalve (Figure 15). The volume of collected exhaled water cleared of particles per unit time was calculated as $Y = Fl(1 - C_e/C_i)$, where Fl is the flow rate through the glass tube and C_e and C_i are the concentrations of algal cells in the water simultaneously collected in the exhalant and inhalant currents. At the proper (high) flow rate, the clearance equals the filtration rate. With this method filtration rates can be determined in undisturbed, infaunal bivalves.

[38]

Winter (1973) developed an apparatus for the feeding of filter-feeding bivalves at constant food concentration. The apparatus was subsequently improved by Riisgård & Møhlenberg (1979). In the apparatus (Figure 16) water from the photoaquarium is pumped with high speed through the mussel chamber to prevent recirculation, and algal concentration is kept nearly constant by means of a photocell-circuit that starts and stops the dosing pump when the concentration exceeds a preset range. Variation in concentration as well as dosing of algal culture are recorded.

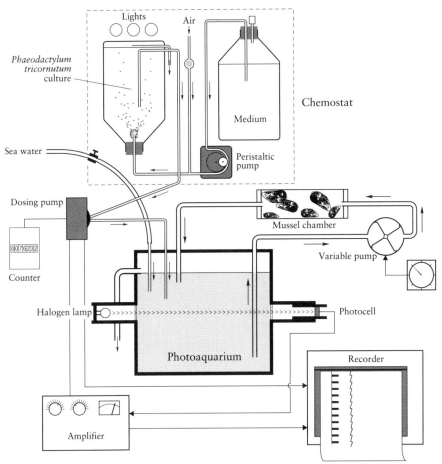

Figure 16. Diagram of apparatus for automatically recording rates of water processing in e.g. *Mytilus edulis* at constant algal concentrations (from Riisgård & Møhlenberg, 1979).

More recently fluorometric sensing has been introduced as a means both to record number of particles and to distinguish between kinds of particles, e.g., different types of algal cells, according to their fluorescence (Gallager & Mann, 1980; Shumway *et al.*, 1985, 1988; Winter, 1978).

An extensive literature deals with the rates at which filter-feeding bivalves process the ambient water. The literature has been reviewed several times (Ali, 1970; Bayne, Thompson & Widdows, 1976; Jørgensen 1966, 1975b; Morton, 1983). Recorded clearances or rates of water pumping may differ greatly, presumably varying with the experimental conditions. As shown below (p.47), the rates at which filter-feeding bivalves process water is correlated with the gape of the valves. It is argued that reduced gaping and pumping reflect adverse conditions, and that under optimal conditions, including appropriate levels of suspended food particles and silt, water is constantly processed at the inherent capacity of the pump. Only rates obtained under presumably optimal conditions have therefore been considered. Examples are shown in Table 10, p. 86, including species where the rates of water processing have been determined as a function of body mass. Rates of water processing and factors affecting the rates are discussed below.

CHAPTER IX

Characteristics of the filter pump

The filter-feeding bivalve may be viewed as an integrated filter pump where knowledge about the pump is essential for an understanding of the filter mechanism. We may distinguish between the pump proper and the system of afferent and efferent canals, as indicated in the diagram in Figure 17. The bands of lateral cilia constitute the pump. In reality the pump consists of a large number of small pumps arranged in parallel. The canal system includes the flow path from the inhalant opening through the mantle cavity to the entrance to the interfilament canals on the upstream side of the pump, and the interfilament canals, demibranchial lumina, suprabranchial cavity and exhalant siphon on the downstream side.

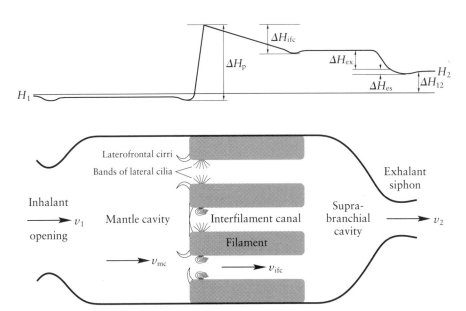

Figure 17. *Mytilus edulis*. Diagrams of the mussel pump and of static pressures along the flow path. v_1, flow velocity in inhalant opening; v_2, flow velocity in exhalant siphon; v_{ifc}, flow velocity in interfilament canals; v_{mc}, flow velocity in mantle cavity (from Jørgensen , 1989).

A pump is characterized by the relationship between the pressure rise delivered by the pump, ΔH_p, and the pumping rate, V. This relationship, the pump characteristic, is not directly accessible for analysis, but it may be approached indirectly through studies of the relationships between pressure resistances exerted by the system, ΔH_{sys}, and pumping rate, the system characteristic. In steady state the pump pressure equals the system resistance, $\Delta H_p = \Delta H_{sys}$.

In a filter-feeding bivalve, such as *Mytilus edulis*, the system resistance can be resolved into several components (Jørgensen *et al.*, 1986b). These components include the frictional resistance in the canal system, ΔH_f, the exit loss, ΔH_{ex}, as well as the resistance offered by the laterofrontal cirri beating against the through current, ΔH_{lf}. To these may be added a hydrostatic pressure difference between exit and inlet, $H_2 - H_1 = \Delta H_{12}$. A positive ΔH_{12} constitutes a back pressure. Thus,

$$\Delta H_p = \Delta H_f + \Delta H_{ex} + \Delta H_{lf} + \Delta H_{12}. \tag{1}$$

[*41*]

Figure 17 shows schematically the location and relative values of these contributions to the variation in static pressure H along the flow path through a mussel. At the level of the pump, H increases due to energy transfer from the bands of lateral cilia.

The relations between pumping rate and the component resistances have been approached by means that varied with the type of resistance.

Frictional loss in canal system (ΔH_f). The frictional loss in the canal system includes several contributions, varying strongly in importance. Often their absolute values can only be estimated with varying degree of certainty. However, frictional losses in inhalant and exhalant siphons are accessible to direct measurements. As flow through mussels is laminar (Jørgensen *et al.*, 1986a), the cumulative frictional loss in the canal system is presumably a linear function of the flow rate, that is,

$$\Delta H_f = C_f V, \tag{2}$$

where C_f, the frictional coefficient, is the slope of ΔH_f versus pumping rate V (Figure 18, Eq. 2).

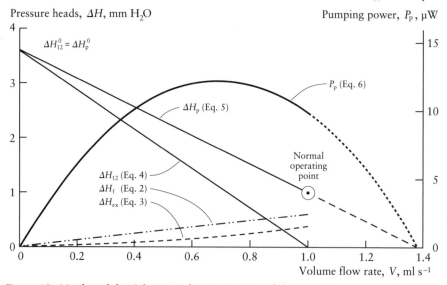

Figure 18. *Mytilus edulis.* Schematic characterization of the mussel pump. ΔH_f, head-flow characteristic for friction, ΔH_{ex}, for exit flow, ΔH_{12}, for back pressure, and ΔH_p, for pump pressure; P_p, pumping rate-power characteristic (after Jørgensen, 1989).

[42]

Exit loss (ΔH_{ex}). In filter-feeding bivalves the through current leaves the exhalant siphon as a jet of water that represents a loss given by $\Delta H_{ex} = v_2^2/2g$, where v_2 is the velocity at the exit of the siphon and g denotes the acceleration of gravity. $v_2 = V/A_{ex}$, A_{ex} being the cross sectional area of the siphon. The relation may therefore be written

$$\Delta H_{ex} = C_{ex}V^2 , \tag{3}$$

where $C_{ex} = (2gA_{ex}^2)^{-1}$ (Figure 18, Eq. 3). Because ΔH_{ex} is a quadratic function of V, the relative importance of the exit loss increases with the pumping rate.

Laterofrontal cirri (ΔH_{lf}). As mentioned, the nature and magnitude of the resistance to flow offered by the laterofrontal cirri have been a matter of debate. The question was elucidated by determination of the effects of 5-hydroxytryptamine (serotonin) on the back-pressure flow characteristic of mussels (Jørgensen *et al.*, 1986b). Serotonin is a nerve transmitter in the bivalve gill, and added to the ambient water it will affect the functioning of the cirri (Jørgensen, 1976a). Normally, the cirri beat through an angle of 90° (Figure 13), but in *Mytilus edulis* serotonin at high concentration reduces the angle of beat of the cirri which remain more or less fixed at the end of

20 µm

Laterofrontal cirri

Lateral cilia

Figure 19. Scanning electron micrograph of 10^{-6} mol/l serotonin stimulated gill fragment of *Mytilus edulis*, surface view of two filaments. The laterofrontal cirri are maximally bent over the frontal surfaces of the filaments, pointing towards the tips of the filaments. The lateral cilia were active at fixation. Their organisation in metachronal waves can be clearly seen (from Jørgensen, 1975a).

the effective stroke, bent over the frontal surface of the filaments, as shown in Figure 19 (Jørgensen, 1975a; Sanderson *et al.*, 1985). By exposing mussels to 10^{-5} mol/l serotonin the cirri are effectively removed from the path of the currents entering the interfilament canals, thus eliminating their contribution to the frictional loss as well as any flow-independent head loss. Such elimination did not measurably affect the back-pressure flow characteristic, and the contribution of ΔH_{1f} to the pump characteristic may be disregarded (Jørgensen *et al.*, 1988).

Back pressure (ΔH_{12}). The back pressure is the positive hydrostatic pressure difference between exit and inlet, $H_2 - H_1 = \Delta H_{12}$ (Figure 17). In nature pressure differences between exit and inlet depends on the ambient pattern of water currents. As argued in the chapter on passive filter feeding (p. 101) they are presumably unimportant in bivalves. In the laboratory, arbitrary positive and negative values of ΔH_{12} may be externally imposed.

The nature of the relation between imposed back pressure and flow rate, the back-pressure flow characteristic, cannot be predicted theoretically, but it can be approached experimentally, and determination of the back-pressure flow characteristic under various functional states of the mussel has been an essential tool in elucidating the performance characteristics of the gill pump. The relationship between back pressure and pumping rate was determined in the set-up described in the chapter on measurements of pumping rates (Figure 14, p. 36).

The relationships between back pressure and pumping rate could be described as linear functions (Figure 18, Eq. 4)

$$\Delta H_{12} = \Delta H_{12}{}^0 - C_{12}V, \tag{4}$$

where $\Delta H_{12}{}^0$ is the back pressure at which water ceases to flow through the system, indicated by the intersection of the ordinate, and the coefficient $C_{12} = \Delta H_{12}{}^0/V^0$ is the slope of the characteristic, where V^0 is the flow rate at zero back pressure, indicated by the intersection of the abscissa.

The pump characteristic. The relationships between component resistances and pumping rate, the component characteristics, define the pump characteristic. These relationships may now be written as

$$\Delta H_{\mathrm{p}} = \Delta H_{12}{}^0 - (C_{12} - C_{\mathrm{f}})V + C_{\mathrm{ex}}V^2. \tag{5}$$

[*44*]

The pump characteristic is thus determined by two linear and one quadratic term. In conditions where the exit loss is small compared with the other resistance losses, the pump head pressure thus approximates a linear function of pumping rate (Figure 18, Eq. 5). A linear characteristic is to be expected for a low Reynolds number viscous pump.

In assessing the properties of a pump it is of particular interest to know the normal operating point, that is, the pressure when no back pressure is imposed on the pump. This pressure was calculated to be about 1 mm H_2O in an optimally pumping, fully open mussel at 17 °C (Table 3). According

Table 3. *Mytilus edulis*. Pumping rate and predominant head losses in an optimally pumping 35 mm 'standard' mussel at the reference temperature (t_r) of 17, 10 and 5 °C, calculated from a viscous, leaky, constant-force pump model (from Jørgensen *et al.*, 1990)

Temperature (°C)	17	10	5
Pumping rate V(ml min^{-1})	65	56.84	50.67
Head losses ΔH(mm H_2O)			
Frictional losses			
Interfilament canals ΔH_{ifc}	0.34	0.356	0.366
Exhalant siphon ΔH_{es}	0.18	0.161	0.146
Kinetic loss			
Exhalant siphon ΔH_{ex}	0.44	0.336	0.267
Total	0.96	0.85	0.78

to these calculations, the interfilament canals and exhalant siphon constitute the most important contributions to the head losses. The estimates for the frictional head losses in the inhalant opening and exhalant siphon, based on boundary layer friction, are lower than direct measurements reported by Jones & Allen (1986). They obtained values of 0.54 ± 0.18 (SD) mm H_2O and 1.23 ± 0.48 mm H_2O for head losses across inhalant opening and exhalant siphon, respectively, values that are an order of magnitude higher than those Foster-Smith (1976) obtained using a less advanced technique.

Similar discrepancies also apply to other bivalves, such as the cockle *Cerastoderma edule* and the soft clam *Mya arenaria* (Foster-Smith, 1976; Jones & Allen, 1986). In *M. arenaria*, the inhalant and exhalant siphons are long tubes of approximately constant, circular cross sectional area along their entire length, so the frictional head losses could be calculated from the Poiseuille equation $\Delta H_s = 8VvL/\pi a^4 g$ cm H_2O, where V is the pumping rate

[45]

in ml s^{-1}, ν is the kinematic viscosity of water (= 0.012 stokes at 12 °C), L is the siphon length in cm, a is the radius of the siphon lumen in cm, and g is the acceleration of gravity. Calculations made on a clam that pumped about 1 ml s^{-1} with the siphons extended to a length of 10 cm amounted to ≤ 1 mm H$_2$O. This low value for the frictional resistance to flow even in long siphons is consistent with the finding that excision of the siphons did not measurably affect the rate of pumping, indicating that the siphonal resistance to flow is low (Jørgensen & Riisgård, 1988).

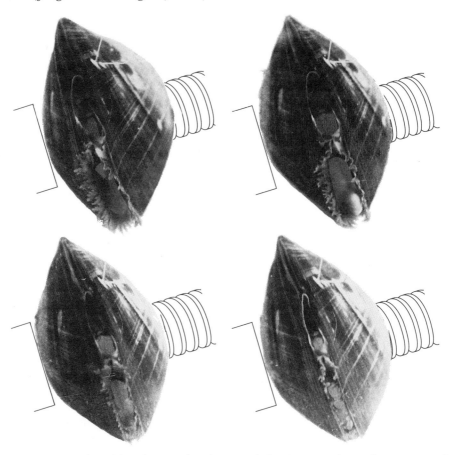

Figure 20. *Mytilus edulis*. Photographs of a mussel showing extension and orientation of mantle edges and exhalant siphon under progressively reduced gaping of the valves, passively controlled by turning the screw. Diameter of the screw is 7.2 mm (from Jørgensen *et al.*, 1988).

Valve gape and pump characteristics

Pumping rates vary with the degree of gaping of the valves, from zero to a maximum rate characteristic of the fully open state (Jørgensen *et al.*, 1988). Reduction in valve gape is accompanied by retraction of the mantle edges and expiratory siphon, including reduced area of the siphon aperture. Figure 20 shows the relations between passively reduced valve gape and orientation of mantle edges and siphon in an otherwise undisturbed mussel. Pumping rate thus varies both with valve gape and area of siphon aperture, as shown in Figure 21. But the relationship between valve gape and pumping rate is not well defined, suggesting that the relationship is of an indirect nature.

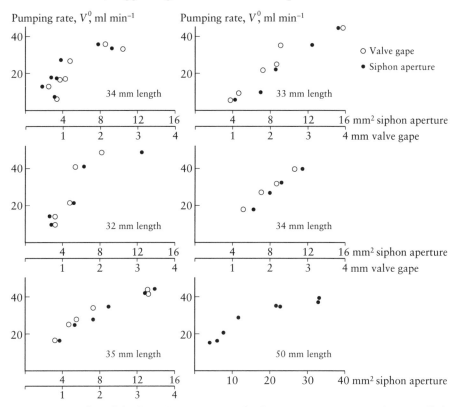

Figure 21. *Mytilus edulis*. Pumping rate at zero back pressure versus passively controlled valve gape and area of siphon aperture in six mussels ranging in length from 32 to 50 mm (from Jørgensen *et al.*, 1988).

[47]

Back pressure, ΔH_{12}, mm H_2O

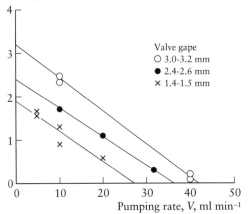

Figure 22. *Mytilus edulis.* Effects of actively reduced valve gape on the back-pressure flow characteristic. The regression lines are shown (from Jørgensen *et al.*, 1988).

Table 4. *Mytilus edulis.* Relations between back pressure at zero flow, ΔH^0_{12}, and gill area specific pumping rate at zero back pressure V^0, in mussels at 10-16 °C: effects of reduced valve gape (means ± SD) (from Jørgensen *et al.*, 1988)

Valve gape	ΔH^0_{12}, mm H_2O	V^0, ml cm^{-2} min^{-1}	$\Delta H^0_{12}/V^0 = C_{12}$	n
Optimal	3.5±0.32	3.7±0.45	0.94±0.11	8
Reduced	2.6 (1.6-3.7)	2.8 (2.2-3.6)	0.90 (0.74-1.04)	3

The relationship between valve gape and properties of the pump could be further elucidated by the effects of reduced valve gape on the back-pressure flow characteristic. Figure 22 and Table 4 show that pump power and pumping rate were reduced proportionately at reduced valve gape (Jørgensen *et al.*, 1988). The reduction in pump power is thus the predominant effect of a reduced gaping of the valves. This was a counterintuitive result. It is generally taken for granted that the declining pumping rates at reduced valve gape result from increasing frictional resistances. It therefore became crucial to understand the causal relationship between valve gape and pump power.

Extension of mantle edges and expiratory siphon is closely coupled to the valve gape, indicating coordinated activity of the muscular systems that control the two states. The extension of the mantle and siphon may also be determined by the geometry of the space between the two valves, the reduced gaping of the valves limiting extension (Figure 20). The relative importance of coordinated activity of the muscles and pure physical constraint

[48]

in establishing the relations between valve gape and extension of mantle and siphon remains to be assessed.

Varying extension of mantle and siphon, secondary to the gaping of the valves, may affect the gill pump by affecting interfilament distances. The muscles that retract mantle and siphon are continuous with muscles running along the bases of the gills at their attachment to the body wall. Retraction of mantle and siphon results in shortening of the gill axes and thus of the demibranchs. This shortening is partitioned among the interfilament canals with no change in the width of the filaments. Retraction of mantle and siphon thus concurrently reduces the space between opposite bands of lateral cilia. This can be observed in preparations where one valve and the underlying mantle have been removed (Figure 23). In such preparations opposite bands of lateral cilia are typically approaching each other to the extent that the metachronal waves running along the actively beating bands of cilia may interfere during their effective strokes. Complete retraction of the mantle and siphon may thus reduce the distance between the tips of opposite lateral cilia during the phase of beat when they are oriented perpendicularly on the filament surface from about 10 μm to about zero. Also in other filter-feeding

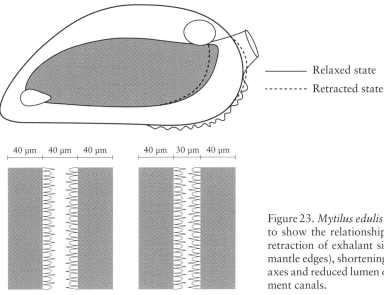

————— Relaxed state

- - - - - - - - Retracted state

40 μm 40 μm 40 μm   40 μm 30 μm 40 μm

Relaxed state   Retracted state

Figure 23. *Mytilus edulis*. Diagrams to show the relationships between retraction of exhalant siphon (and mantle edges), shortening of the gill axes and reduced lumen of interfilament canals.

[49]

bivalves the width of the interfilament canals vary with the length of the gill axes, the length of which again varies with the valve gape and extension of mantle edges (Jørgensen & Riisgård, 1988, and personal observations).

Probably, it is this reduction in width of the interfilament canals, ultimately derived from reduced gaping of the valves, which is responsible for the concurrent reduction in power and capacity of the gill pump. Such a conclusion is also in accordance with dynamic properties that can be ascribed to the pump proper, as argued below.

Effects of temperature

A large literature deals with effects of temperature on pumping rates in filter-feeding bivalves, reviewed, e.g., by Ali (1970), Schulte (1975), de Villiers *et al.* (1989) and Winter (1978). Typically, results are inconsistent, correlated with lack of information about the behaviour of the animals, whether fully open or partially closed. The acute effects of temperature on pumping rates were recently re-evaluated in mussels, *Mytilus edulis*, seasonally acclimatized to temperatures ranging from 6 °C in February to 12 °C in June (Jørgensen *et al.*, 1990). The temperature ranges adopted were those tolerated by the mussels, that is, within which they remained fully open, indicating that they pumped water at the capacity of the pump. In the cold adapted mussels in February the upper temperature tolerated was 16 °C, against 22 °C in June. In the lower range, the cold adapted mussels tolerated temperatures approaching zero, whereas the 12 °C adapted mussels began to reduce the valve gape or to close up at 4-5 °C.

The relationships between temperature and pumping rate, as based on 17 and 25 measurements, respectively in February and June, tended to be curved (Figure 24 A), consistent with the finding that in the February experiment the slope of linear regression of pumping rate on temperature from 2 to 6 °C was significantly higher than from 6 to 16 °C ($P < 0.02$).

Part of the variation in pumping rate with temperature may be due to changes in the viscosity of the water which affects the resistance to water flow in the canal systems of the mussel pump. This contribution may be estimated from the relationship between pumping rate and viscosity. The regression parameters, listed in Table 5, indicate a close inverse linear relationship between pumping and viscosity. Figure 24 B, moreover, indicates that

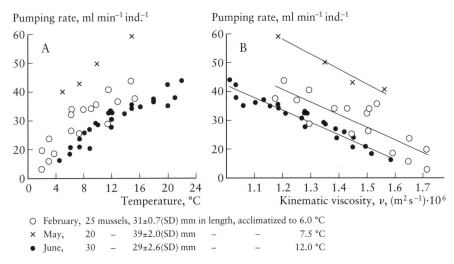

Figure 24. *Mytilus edulis*. A: Relationship between clearance of algal cells (= pumping rate) and temperature in groups of mussels at different times of the year. B: Relationship between pumping rate and temperature-dependent kinetic viscosity, ν, of sea water in the groups of mussels shown in A (from Jørgensen *et al.*, 1990).

Table 5. *Mytilus edulis*. Linear regression of pumping rate, V, (ml min^{-1} ind^{-1}) on kinematic viscosity of sea water, ν(m^2 s^{-1})·10^6, $V = a + b\nu$, in the groups of mussels shown in Figure 24. Viscosity as a function of temperature is given by Rawson & Tupper (1968).

Month	Tempera-rature range, °C	Regression parameters a	b	r	Number of measure-ments
February	2-16	92.4	−43.1	−0.836	17
May	5-15	120.8	−52.3	−0.985	4
June	4-22	84.9	−42.8	−0.951	25

this relationship encompasses the whole temperature range within which the mussels remained fully open. Thus, little room was left for other factors than viscosity in influencing the rate of water pumping, such as the frequency of beating of the lateral cilia. As discussed below, ciliary beat frequencies vary with temperature, implying that substantial changes in beat frequencies of the lateral cilia have no obvious effect on the pumping rate.

[*51*]

Data obtained by Loosanoff (1958) on pumping rates in fully open oysters, *Crassostrea virginica*, agree closely with those obtained in mussels (Jørgensen *et al.*, 1990).

Studies on effects of temperature on the pump characteristic showed that maximum pressures at zero pumping, ΔH_{12}^{0} ($= \Delta H_{p}^{0}$) was independent of the temperature, being 3.15 ± 0.30 (SD) mm H_2O at 5 °C and 3.19 ± 0.32 mm H_2O at 15 °C. Operating point, however, declined moderately with temperature (Table 3, p. 45) (Jørgensen *et al.*, 1990).

Absence of temperature acclimation. The effect of temperatures on pumping rates obtained in acute experiments was confirmed in mussels at the temperatures of acclimatization, about 8 °C in December and about 17 °C in August (Jørgensen *et al.*, 1986b, 1988, 1990; H.U. Riisgård, personal communication). This lack of temperature acclimation in water pumping is contrary to results reported by Widdows & Bayne (1971) who found effective temperature acclimation in mussels within a temperature range from 5 to 20 °C. When mussels were transferred to a higher or lower temperature filtration rates increased or decreased, but returned to the original level within 2-3 weeks. These contrasting results between none and full temperature acclimation in water pumping in mussels remain to be explained. It is, however, noteworthy that in Widdows & Bayne's (1971) experiments the mussels were filtering water at low rates, varying between 10 and 30% of that characteristic of fully open mussels (Table 10, p. 86).

Modelling of the pump

The pump consists of bands of diaplectically beating cilia (Aiello & Sleigh, 1972; Knight-Jones, 1954). The bands are about 10 μm broad, in *Mytilus edulis* comprising about 25 cilia. The cilia are thus densely spaced, both across and along the bands. Moreover, the bands are of virtually infinite length compared with the width, extending from base to tip of the filaments, or more than one cm in large mussels. So far there appears to be no theoretical study of cilia arranged in narrow bands. Existing theories either consider ciliated surfaces of infinite or large extent or they consider a single flagellum or cilium (see, for example, the review of Brennen & Winet, 1977). Two types of model have been proposed for the hydrodynamics of ciliated surfaces, especially in ciliates, the sublayer model and the envelope model (Blake & Sleigh, 1975, Brennen & Winet, 1977).

The sublayer model is based on the interactions between individual cilia and the surrounding water, and it applies to systems composed of widely spaced cilia, an order of 1 cilium-length apart. The envelope model assumes that the cilia are so closely packed that they interact with the surrounding water primarily through the oscillating surface that envelopes the metachronal wave of the ciliary system (Brennen & Winet, 1977). In the bands constituting the mussel gill pump the cilia are arranged in rows that run obliquely across the band. The rows form angles of about 40° with the normal across the band (Aiello & Sleigh, 1972). The cilia are spaced 0.2 μm apart both across and along the band. During the effective stroke the cilia are fanned out and the interciliary distance increases to about 1 μm between the tips of the 15 μm long cilia. However, an effective stroke comprises several rows of metachronally beating fanned-out cilia (Aiello & Sleigh, 1972), so that the distances between the tips of neighbouring cilia amount to only small fractions of 1 μm. The currents of water moving through the interfilament canals almost exclusively pass distal to the tips of the cilia. It therefore seems that a hydrodynamic theory for the bivalve pump should be based on an envelope model of finite extent (Jørgensen, 1982).

Silvester (1988) estimated the maximum pressure exerted by the mussel gill pump under the assumption that the pump unit is the individual lateral cilium. He arrived at the value of 8 Pa, or 0.8 mm H_2O, that is, about one fifth of the actually measured pressure produced by fully open mussels at zero flow. It is thus indicated that the pump cannot be reduced to the individual cilia, supporting the concept that the pump unit is the opposing oscillating surfaces enveloping the bands of lateral cilia.

In the envelope model of infinite extent the oscillatory motions of the effectively material surface produce a steady current of water tangential to the surface (Brennen & Winet, 1977). In a stationary ciliate, *Spirostomum* sp., Cheung & Winet (1975) found that the velocity of the current attained its highest value at 1-1.5 cilium-lengths from the ciliated surface. This maximum velocity persisted beyond 2 cilium-lengths before tapering slowly. We do not know at what distance from the surface the current passing a band of lateral cilia attains its maximum velocity. However, consider that the cilia extend about 15 μm from the filament surface during the effective stroke, leaving a central gap of only about 10 μm in a 40 μm wide interfilament canal. Obviously, the velocity distributions generated by the opposing bands of cilia must interfere significantly. In the fully open mussel this interference may be positive (Niels Finnerup Nielsen, personal communication). Such positive interaction is supported by the observations that, whereas water currents produced by maximally activated single bands of lateral cilia amounts to only about 1 mm s^{-1} (Sleigh & Aiello, 1972) or 2-3 mm s^{-1} (Jørgensen, 1982), the mean interfilament currents at the level of the lateral cilia in intact fully open mussels can be estimated to be about 6 mm s^{-1}, or faster than the speed of the tips of the cilia during the effective stroke (Jørgensen, 1982).

Presumably, interference becomes negative with decreasing width of the interfilament canals, resulting from reduced valve gape. It is to be expected that the pump characteristic will change, yielding a smaller pressure rise and smaller pumping rate, as actually observed and theoretically inferred (Jørgensen et al., 1988).

The linear relationship between back pressure and flow rate in the Mytilus pump indicates that the power of a ciliary pump is unaffected by the resistance offered to flow whether the resistance is due to an imposed back pressure or increased systemic frictional resistance. The reduction in pump power with decreasing valve gape could therefore not have been predicted as a result of increased systemic frictional resistance. This inference is supported by comparison of the bivalve pump with another ciliary pump. The properties of an ascidian pump have been analysed by Riisgård (1988b) in Styela clava. The back-pressure flow rate characteristic is linear, as in M. edulis, but the maximum pressure, amounting to about 1 mm H$_2$O, was independent of the flow rate.

In ascidians, the pump proper is located in the ostia that perforate the pharynx wall. The through current is produced by ciliary tracts lining the inside of the ostia. The dimensions of the ostia, and thus the geometry of the pump, is more fixed than the bivalve pump. Characteristics of the ascidian pump thus provides additional evidence for the importance of the geometry, especially the distance between opposing ciliary bands, for the force the ciliary pump can exert on the ambient water. Decline in pump power with reduced flow rate, V^0, is thus not an emergent property of a ciliary pump generally, but of a collapsible ciliary pump, such as the bivalve gills.

Summing up, the capacity of the pump in filter-feeding bivalves can be fully utilized only in relaxed animals with extended mantle edges and siphons. Importantly, this is the behaviour adopted by undisturbed animals in the presence of seston, including food particles, suspended in the ambient water. Rates of water processing decline concurrently with the reduction in width of the interfilament canals. This reduction is a secondary result of reduced valve gape, correlated with shortening of the length of the gill axes. Excessive relaxation of the musculature, e.g., under spawning or artificially induced by serotonin stimulation (Jørgensen et al., 1988), does not, or only moderately, enhance water pumping. It is thus indicated that the pump, particularly the distance between the opposing bands of lateral cilia, is dimensioned for the largest favourable hydrodynamic effect of interaction between the opposing bands of cilia when the animal is relaxed.

The ill-defined relation between valve gape and water pumping reflects the indirect nature of the relation between width of the interfilament canals, extension of mantle edges and valve gape. Reduced pumping rates with decreasing valve gape therefore does not appear to constitute a physiological mechanism to control the rate of water processing. Rather, reduced gaping of the valves reflects suboptimal or adverse environmental conditions.

Beat frequency of lateral cilia and pumping rates

The normal frequency of beating of the lateral cilia has been measured in young transparent mussels and other bivalves (Dral, 1977; Jørgensen & Ockelmann, 1990) and in large mussels after severing of the adductor muscle and exposure of the gill in situ (Aiello, 1960; Stefano et al., 1977). In such preparations the activity of the lateral cilia continues, whereas activity rapidly declines in excised gills or in gill fragments (Gray, 1928; Aiello, 1960).

The activity of the lateral cilia in intact gills is typically erratic, and in Dral's (1977) observations of young mussels the spontaneous, irregular fluctuations in beat frequency overshadowed any effect of temperature. Further observations of young bivalves, including Mytilus edulis, did, however, show that mean beat frequencies increased from about 10 Hz at 14 °C, the temperature of acclimatization, to about 15 Hz or more at 20-21 °C, corresponding to Q_{10} values of about 2 (Jørgensen & Ockelmann, 1990).

In large mussels with the gills left in situ after removal of the valves the beat frequency of the lateral cilia varied from about 7 at 2 °C to about 22 at

[55]

23 °C, corresponding to a Q_{10} = 1.8 (Aiello, 1960). In freshly opened mussels in the field, Stefano et al. (1977) observed a diurnal cycle in beat frequency varying from about 8 to 16 Hz, correlated with the temperature cycle of an amplitude of about 4 °C (read from their Figure 1). This would imply a Q_{10} of about 5-6. In mussels followed in the field at environmental temperatures that increased from 14 °C in early June to 22 °C in late July, the beat frequency of the lateral cilia increased from about 10 to about 18 Hz (read from their Figure 2), corresponding to a Q_{10} of 1.8.

Cessation of activity of the lateral cilia in the excised gill presumably results from interruption of the serotonergic innervation of the gill filaments, and normal beating may be restored by addition of serotonin to the medium (Aiello, 1960; Catapane et al., 1978; Gosselin, 1961; Gosselin et al., 1962). The beat frequency after serotonin stimulation varied with the temperature (Catapane et al., 1981; Jørgensen et al., 1990). Table 6 shows the effects of temperature and serotonin on beat frequency of the lateral cilia in gill frag-

Table 6. *Modiolus modiolus*. Effects of temperature and serotonin on frequency of beat of the lateral cilia in gill fragments (means ± SD) (from Jørgensen et al., 1990).

Temperature, °C	Serotonin concentration, M	Beat frequency, Hz	Q_{10}
11	10^{-7}	10.3 ± 0.3	2.1
21		21.4 ± 2.1	
11	10^{-6}	14.0 ± 1.6	2.0
21		27.5 ± 2.5	
11	10^{-5}	15.7 ± 0.3	2.0
21		31.0 ± 1.5	

ments of *Modiolus modiolus* at the concentrations 10^{-7}, 10^{-6} and 10^{-5} mol/l. 10^{-7} mol/l serotonin restored a normal activity level in isolated gill fragments of *Mytilus edulis* whereas 10^{-5} mol/l produced maximum beat frequency (Clemmesen & Jørgensen, 1987). Throughout the concentration range the temperature effect was the same, corresponding to a Q_{10} = 2. When serotonin was added to the ambient water at 17 °C at concentrations ranging from 10^{-6} to 10^{-4} mol/l the beat frequencies, as measured immediately upon excision of gill fragments, were 22 ± 2.1 (SD) at 10^{-6} mol/l serotonin, 26 ± 2.1 at 10^{-5} mol/l and 26 ± 1.1 at 10^{-4} mol/l. Maximum stimulation was thus obtained at 10^{-5} mol/l serotonin also in 'intact' mussels. The Q_{10} values were of the same order as those measured in the gill fragments of *Modiolus modiolus*, viz., 2.1 at 10^{-6} mol/l serotonin and 2.3 at 10^{-5} mol/l in the temperature interval 11 to 17 °C, and 1.7 and 1.6, respectively, in the interval 17 to 21 °C.

Thus, the effect of temperature on the activity of the lateral cilia maintained at constant serotonin stimulation, mimicking the normal cilio-excitatory serotonergic innervation, did not differ from the effect on the spontaneous activity in intact mussels.

This effect of temperature on the beat frequency of the lateral cilia may be compared with that on other ciliary systems of the gill, namely the frontal ciliary tract of the filaments and the ciliary tract in the food groove along the ventral margins of the demibranchs. In these systems the beat frequency was not measured directly, but the effect was inferred from the changes in velocity of particles suspended in the currents generated by the activity of the ciliary tracts, the particles acting as indicators of the velocity of the currents. The temperature coefficient Q_{10} for the current along the frontal surface of the filament of the *Mytilus edulis* gill decreased from 3.5 at a temperature increase from zero to 5 °C to 2.1 in the temperature interval 20-25 °C (Gray, 1928). In the food groove, the Q_{10} for the increase in particle velocity decreased from 2.2 in the interval 5-10 °C to 1.7 in the interval 15-20 °C (Jørgensen, 1975a). The Q_{10} values for beat frequency of the cilia or the currents generated by the ciliary activity in all three systems are thus typical of chemical (metabolic) processes, rather than physical.

This is in contrast to the effect of temperature on the pumping rates in the intact bivalve where, as mentioned, the change in the viscosity of the water could account for the effect, leaving little space for a specific effect of the increased beat frequency on the pumping rate.

This absence of an increase in water pumping specifically due to the increased beat frequency of the lateral cilia agrees with the lacking effect of serotonin stimulation on the pumping rate in intact mussels (Jørgensen *et al.*, 1986b, 1988).

Retention efficiency

As mentioned, in filter-feeding bivalves that possess well developed latero-frontal cirri the threshold particle size for efficient retention is smaller than in bivalves that lack such cirri (Figure 12 and Table 2, pp. 30-31). It is there-fore noteworthy that serotonin in concentrations that gradually reduce the angle of beat of the laterofrontal cirri in *Mytilus edulis* finally to completely remove them from the entrance to the interfilament canals strongly in-creased the porosity of the gills to small algal cells but only moderately so to larger, 13 μm, algal cells (Figure 25). This observation supports the sug-gestion that the laterofrontal cirri act as 'modulators' in the fluid mechanical

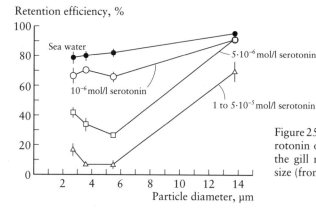

Figure 25. *Mytilus edulis*. Effect of se-rotonin on the efficiency with which the gill retains particles differing in size (from Jørgensen *et al.*, 1986b).

processes responsible for the transfer of particles from the through currents into the surface currents by increasing the efficiency of the capture mech-anism at the low end of the retention spectrum. High concentrations of sero-tonin that caused supernormal relaxation of the musculature (Jørgensen *et al.*, 1988) also reduced the efficiency of retention of the larger particles.

The serotonin-induced increase in the threshold of size of efficiently re-tained particles may not be solely a simple effect of removing the beating laterofrontal cirri from the path of the through currents. Serotonin also sub-stantially alters the flow patterns at the entrance to the canals, which may determine the efficiency of particle retention, both by greatly increasing fre-quency and amplitude of the oscillating currents produced by the bands of lateral cilia and by changing the beat of the laterofrontal cirri (Jørgensen, 1975a, 1982).

CHAPTER X

Adaptations, exaptations and physical consequences

The word adaptation has several meanings. As pointed out by Williams (1966) the term may even be used for characters and properties that arose fortuitously in the process of natural selection. We should therefore distinguish between emergent properties and true adaptations. Even in this narrower sense, the term adaptation covers two kinds of phenomena. Adaptation is used for a character or property that arose through evolution for its current use. But characters may also have originated as adaptations, to have been turned during evolution to their current use, or characters may not originally have constituted adaptations at all. Such adaptations have been called pre-adaptations, with a teleological tinge. Gould & Vrba (1982) recognized the need for a better term, and they suggested the word exaptation, that is, characters that are '*fit (aptus) by reason of (ex)* their form, or *exaptus*'.

Filter-feeding in bivalves provides many examples of how adaptations and exaptations integrate with physical consequences in establishing complex interplays between an organism and its environment. An analysis of this interplay may, moreover, elucidate basic features in the evolution of ciliary filter feeding.

Originally, ciliation of the molluscan gill probably constituted an adaptation that served to produce the respiratory water current and to clean the gills of particles retained from the respiratory current (Yonge, 1947). Such cleaning systems use mucus for binding of particles and as a vehicle for their transport along rejection tracts.

The cleaning mechanism involves ciliation of the frontal surfaces of the gill filaments. When densely spaced on a surface in contact with water, active cilia tend to establish metachronal waves and to produce a water current along the ciliated surface. This seems to be due to viscous forces acting between cilia and water (Gray, 1930; Machemer, 1974). Frontal surface currents may thus arise as a consequence of the physical properties inherent to a ciliated surface. As mentioned, it is also a physical property of a laminar current along a wall such as the gill surface to retain suspended particles within the current at distances from the wall that are determined by forces acting between the particles and the wall. These forces both prevent particles from direct contact with the wall, as well as from escaping from the surface current. The ability of ciliated surface currents to carry particles may thus be interpreted as an exaptation for the transport of captured food particles in suspension, whereas the fluid mechanical mechanism of transport is a physical consequence of the establishment of ciliated frontal surfaces on the molluscan gill, a feature which originally served to clean the gill.

The establishment of the bivalve gill as a food collecting structure required a substantial increase in pumping rate because of the low concentrations of food particles in the ambient water. This change from a respiratory current to a feeding current constitutes an adaptation.

It is a basic feature of the bivalve gill that the laminar currents passing through the interfilament canals and the currents along the frontal surfaces of the filaments at the level of intersection of the two systems establish hydrodynamic forces that tend to move particles suspended in the through current across streamlines into the surface currents. This mechanism of capture of food particles thus originated in principle as an emergent property of the low Reynolds number fluid mechanics applying to the gill currents. There is a striking parallelism qua emergent properties between filtration in the bivalve gill and the filtration of pollen from the air in wind-pollinated plants, based on high Reynolds number fluid mechanics (Niklas, 1985).

Many groups of suspension-feeding bivalves possess a third ciliary system on the gills, the laterofrontal cirri, whose activity contributes to the current along the frontal surface of the filaments. Presumably, the laterofrontal cirri act to improve the efficiency with which the gills retain particles in the lower end of the size range of suspended particles. The cirri thus constitute adaptations to feed on the smallest phytoplankton organisms.

This basic complex of adaptations, exaptations and emergent properties may be supplemented with additional features. A crucial one seems to be the location of the bands of lateral cilia close to the entrance to the interfilament canals. The oscillatory currents enveloping the bands of lateral cilia may constitute the hydrodynamic basis for the efficient transfer of suspended particles from the through currents into the surface currents. The location of the bands of lateral cilia may thus be an adaptation to filter feeding.

The original cleaning function of the surface currents of the respiratory gills by rejection of particles bound to mucus is maintained in the food-collecting gills. The mucus forms thin strings passing down the gill surface to the ventral margins of the gill filaments. This structural feature of mucus, forming strings traversing numerous gill filaments, is fundamental to the feeding mechanism because it permits the simultaneous transfer of particles bound in mucus for rejection and particles suspended in the surface current for ingestion. The aggregation of numerous contributions from individual mucus cells into distinct mucus strings presumably depends upon the visco-elastic properties of mucus. The establishment of simultaneous retention of suspended food and rejection of a surplus of suspended particles may thus be considered as a physico-chemical consequence. However, the secretion of mucus in amounts that are graded in response to the concentration of suspended particles, exhibiting a threshold concentration below which mucus is not secreted, constitutes an adaptation in filter feeding.

CHAPTER XI

Energetics of the bivalve pump

The energetics of the bivalve pump may be studied at several levels: (1) power output from the pump, dissipated as systemic frictional heat or delivered as kinetic energy in the jet current from the exhalant siphon, representing external work done; (2) energy consumed by the beating of the lateral cilia, constituting the pump proper; (3) energy consumed by the cells carrying the bands of lateral cilia; (4) energy consumed by the gills, constituting the water processing structure; and (5) energy consumed by the global pump, the intact, water-processing bivalve. This hierarchy gives rise to a number of efficiencies of energy transfer between levels.

The power output, P_p, from the pump is determined by the pumping rate, V, and operating pressure, ΔH_p. In the mussel, the pumping-rate power characteristic could be described as a parabola, $P_p = \rho g(\Delta H_p^0 - C_p V)V$, (Figure 18, p.42), where ΔH_p^0 is the intersection of the ordinate and $C_p = \Delta H_p^0/V^0$, V^0 being the nominal intersection of the abscissa, indicating the potential maximal pumping rate (Jørgensen et al., 1986b, 1988). It may be seen from Figure 18 that the normal operating point is close to that of maximum power. In the 35 mm long 'standard' mussel the pumping power amounted to 10 μW at the normal operating point, against a maximum pumping power of 12 μW reached at $V = 0.69$ ml s^{-1}, corresponding to a back pressure, ΔH_{12}, of 1.1 mm H$_2$O.

Calculated per unit length of bands of lateral cilia the work done at the operating point would be 0.4 μW m^{-1}. Based on calculations of rate of work done by individual cilia in *Paramecium*, Silvester & Sleigh (1984) estimated the power of the ciliary pump of the *Mytilus* gill to 0.15 μW per m of band of lateral cilia.

The greater part of the pumping power is spent on overcoming the frictional resistance in the canal system from entry to exit, kinetic energy in the jet current varying from a small fraction to about one third of the total power output (Jørgensen *et al.*, 1986b, 1988). Compared with the total energy expenditure of the mussel the power output is negligible, in the order of 1 % (Jørgensen *et al.*, 1986b).

The actual energy spent by the pump proper, the bands of lateral cilia and the cells carrying the cilia, is not accessible for direct determination, but Clemmesen & Jørgensen (1987) estimated expenditures, based on the relation between frequency of beating of the lateral cilia and oxygen consumption of fragments of the mussel gill (Figure 26) and on estimates of the proportional consumption of oxygen by the lateral cells. At a beat frequency of 10 Hz, which is representative of undisturbed filter-feeding bivalves (Dral, 1977; Jørgensen & Ockelmann, 1990), the energy consumption of the lateral cells, expressed as synthesis of ATP, amounted to $1.05 \cdot 10^{-10}$ mol ATP cm^{-2} gill area s^{-1}, or 5.1 μW cm^{-2} (1 mol ATP s$^{-1} \sim 4.82 \cdot 10^4$ W).

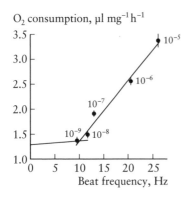

O$_2$ consumption, μl mg^{-1}h^{-1}

Figure 26. *Mytilus edulis*. Relationship between beat frequency of lateral cilia and oxygen consumption of gill fragments. The lower line is the regression line for unstimulated gill fragments, exhibiting beat frequencies ranging from zero to about 12 Hz. The upper line is the regression line for the serotonin-stimulated gill fragments. The figures indicate molar concentrations of serotonin. Vertical bars indicate standard errors of mean rates of oxygen consumption. Standard errors of mean rates of beat frequencies did not exceed the symbols (from Clemmesen & Jørgensen, 1987).

[62]

The rate of synthesis of ATP in the lateral cells should be compared with the rate at which the active cilia hydrolyse ATP. Ciliary activity is based on microtubule sliding between adjacent doublets. The sliding results from dynein molecules on a microtubule passing from binding site to binding site on the adjacent doublet, the sites being spaced at repeat distances of about 24 nm (Satir, 1985, 1989; Satir *et al.*, 1981; Spungin *et al.*, 1987). From knowledge about length and number of lateral cilia, a reliable estimate of binding sites may be obtained. The greatest uncertainty in estimating the rate of ATP hydrolysis arises from ignorance about the number of ATP molecules that are hydrolysed per ciliary beat, estimates ranging from 2 to 9 (Brokaw & Simonick, 1977; Mohri, 1956; Rikmenspoel, 1984; Rikmenspoel *et al.*, 1969). If 2 ATP molecules are hydrolysed per dynein per beat the rate of hydrolysis will amount to $6.06 \cdot 10^{-11}$ mol ATP cm^{-2} s^{-1} (= 2.9 μW cm^{-2}), or 58 % of the rate of synthesis. If 3 ATP molecules are hydrolysed the hydrolysis will increase to 87 % of synthesis. A total of 3 ATP molecules hydrolysed per dynein per beat thus seems to constitute a maximum compatible with a beat frequency of 10 Hz.

Finally, the rate of which ATP is hydrolysed by the active cilia should be compared with the work done in pumping water, amounting to 10 μW in the 35 mm standard mussel. The gill area in a mussel of this size is about 10 cm^2, corresponding to 1 μW cm^{-2} gill area. The work efficiency may thus amount to $(1/2.9) \cdot 100 = 34$ % of ATP hydrolysis.

CHAPTER XII

Is water processing physiologically regulated?

The picture emerging from the studies of the function of the bivalve filter pump may be summarized as follows: At optimal conditions filter-feeding bivalves tend to be fully open and to process water at constant, inherent rates. Deviations from optimal conditions, such as mechanical disturbance and poor water quality or depletion of food and other particles in suspension, provoke partial to complete closure of the valves, resulting in declining to discontinued water processing. No mechanisms for regulation of water processing, e.g. according to physiological (nutritional) needs of the organism, could be demonstrated, variations in pumping rates constituting physical consequences of the interfilament distances that are loosely coupled with the valve gape.

This picture of the function of the bivalve filter pump contrasts with widely held concepts according to which bivalves do control pumping rate and retention efficiency in such a way that ingestion is kept more or less constant under varying concentrations of food in the ambient water. This conjecture may be exemplified by the statement that 'the regulation of food intake and assimilation efficiency [in *Mytilus edulis*], by which the assimilated ration is kept rather constant in a certain range of particle concentrations, is well documented' (Borchardt, 1985).

Feeding rates in filter-feeding bivalves, defined as the rates at which food accumulates in the surface currents of the gills, are determined by the rate of water pumping, efficiency of particle retention and concentration of food particles in the ambient water. The rate of water processing is a basic parameter at the organismic level as well as at the population and ecosystem levels. An evaluation of the evidence proposed for regulation of water pumping and particle retention in filter-feeding bivalves is therefore imperative.

Regulation of beat frequency of lateral cilia

A large literature deals with the innervation of the bivalve gill and nervous regulation of ciliary activity, especially the lateral cilia. The innervation is dual, comprising a cilio-excitatory serotonergic as well as a cilio-inhibitory dopaminergic innervation (Aiello, 1960, 1970; Catapane *et al.*, 1978, 1979; Gosselin, 1961; Murakami, 1987a,b; Paparo, 1985, 1986a,b, 1988; Stefano & Aiello, 1975; Stefano *et al.*, 1977). These two types of innervation have been investigated in preparations by electrical stimulation of the nerves or by application of the neurotransmitters or agonists and antagonists. By these means the rate of beat of the lateral cilia could be controlled within a range from zero to 25-30 Hz.

Obviously, the flow velocity past a band of active lateral cilia varies with the rate of beating of the cilia. It was therefore natural to infer that changes in this rate was a means to regulate the rate of water pumping in the intact

[64]

bivalve, and statements to this effect are mostly left undocumented (Bayne & Newell, 1983, p. 418; Drall, 1977; Hildreth, 1976). Winter (1978), however, refers to a linear relation between ciliary beat s^{-1} (<5->20 Hz) and pumping rate (<10->80 ml g^{-1} h^{-1}) in the oyster *Crassostrea gigas*. Presumably, the correlation is an indirect construction from independent measurements of temperature effects on pumping rate in intact oysters and on ciliary activities in gill preparations. Thus, the data do not warrant drawing conclusions concerning effects of beat frequency of the lateral cilia on rate of water pumping in the intact bivalve.

The activity of the bands of lateral cilia of the gills of filter-feeding bivalves is thus regulated at the cellular level, but the significance of these regulatory mechanisms at the level of the organism is obscure. However, the mechanisms are not involved in a physiological control of the rate of water processing, this rate being insensitive to variation in beat frequency of the lateral cilia.

Constancy of ingestion

Winter (1973) provided more direct evidence for regulation of pumping rates in a filter-feeding bivalve, *Mytilus edulis*, by showing that the long-term rate of ingestion of suspended algae, *Dunaliella marina*, remained constant at a range of algal concentrations from $10 \cdot 10^6$- $40 \cdot 10^6$ l^{-1}. Navarro & Winter (1982) found this capacity for regulation slightly less well developed in the related mussel, *Mytilus chilensis*. In this species ingestion rates increased by 13 and 36 % at increased algal concentrations of 67 and 167 %, respectively. But more or less constant ingestion rates at varying levels of algal suspensions have been recorded from other filter-feeding bivalves, e.g., the scallop *Argopecten irradians* (Palmer, 1980), the oysters *Crassostrea virginica* (Epifanio & Ewart, 1977), *Crassostrea gigas* (Gerdes, 1983) and *Ostrea chilensis* (Winter *et al.*, 1984), and the freshwater mussel *Dreissena polymorpha* (Sprung & Rose, 1988).

The food concentrations used in these experiments ranged from about 1 to 3 mg or more of algal dry mass per litre, corresponding to natural concentrations of seston. The interpretation of constant ingestion rates in terms of physiological regulation of filtration rates is based on the tacit assumption that mussels react to 1-3 mg l^{-1} suspensions of algal culture as they do to

[65]

the same concentrations of natural seston. This assumption is unwarranted, as may be seen by comparison of actual filtration rates.

Winter (1973, 1978) found that at a body mass of 30 mg dry weight, *Mytilus edulis* cleared 1 mg l^{-1} suspensions of *Dunaliella marina* at a rate of 0.18 1 h^{-1}, against 0.10 1 h^{-1} of a 2 mg l^{-1} suspension. These clearances should be compared with the rates at which mussels of the same size clear algal suspensions at natural concentrations of 0.1-0.3 mg dry mass l^{-1}, pure or with silt added. Table 7 shows that addition of silt in concentrations amounting to 5-8 mg l^{-1} substantially increased clearances, to values several times higher than those obtained using Winter's technique. Even as high levels as 17-26 mg l^{-1} of silt enhanced the clearances. Winter (1978) also observed a stimulating effect of silt on the filtration rate. It should be noted that the clearances recorded in Table 7 are mean values for the rates at which

Table 7. *Mytilus edulis.* Average clearances in pure suspensions of *Phaeodactylum tricornutum* and with silt added, referred to a 30 mg mussel (from Kiørboe *et al.*, 1981).

Algal concentration, mg dry wt l^{-1}	Clearance, 1 h^{-1}	+ low silt conc., mg l^{-1}	Clearance, 1 h^{-1}	+ high silt conc., mg l^{-1}	Clearance, 1 h^{-1}	Temperature, °C
0.1	0.56	5.3	0.76	26	0.64	13-14
0.2	0.57	5.7	0.75	17	0.62	13-14
0.3	0.67	8.2	0.96			17

a large batch of mussels filtered water over several weeks (Kiørboe *et al.*, 1981). Presumably therefore declining filtration rates with increasing, high concentrations of algal suspension reflects increasing environmental adversity. Such relationship will automatically result in ingestion rates that vary less than food levels. How much less appears fortuitous rather than regulated. Riisgård (1990) also found that high concentrations of algae (*Rhodomonas baltica*) reduced filtration rates in mussels, but the reduction was independent of the actual concentrations, ranging from $10 \cdot 10^6$ to $40 \cdot 10^6$ cells l^{-1}, supporting the non-regulated nature of the response.

The importance of silt for establishing optimal conditions for water processing may vary between species. Thus, in *Spisula subtruncata* (Møhlenberg & Kiørboe, 1981) and *Mercenaria mercenaria* (Bricelj & Malouf, 1984) the addition of silt to a suspension of algae did not increase the rates at which the animals cleared the water of algal cells.

Retention efficiency

The efficiency with which filter-feeding bivalves retain particles may vary with internal and environmental conditions, including concentration and composition of suspended matter in the ambient water. The variation is expressed in the critical particle size for complete retention. Some authors have assumed that increased leakiness of the gills to small particles constitutes an adaptation towards control over energy acquisition (Bayne & Newell, 1983; Bayne et al., 1977; Palmer & Williams, 1980). The factors that determine the efficiency of particle retention are, however, poorly understood and it seems premature to interpret variations in efficiency of particle retention in terms of regulation of food intake.

Costs of water processing

High metabolic costs of pumping water and processing retained particulate material have been used as a teleological argument for control of rates of water processing. It was thus suggested that reduced filtration in the cockle Cardium (Cerastoderma) edule in winter, when inorganic seston levels are high, 'may comprise an adaptive mechanism to reduce the high metabolic costs that would accompany the processing of large amounts of material of low nutritional value by the gills and palps' (Newell & Bayne, 1980). A similar line of thought is expressed by Gerdes (1983) in his studies of filtration rates as a function of food concentration in Crassostrea gigas. He argues that maintenance of high filtering activity resulting in production of pseudofaeces or regulation of assimilation is uneconomic from an ecological point of view because much more energy is needed to maintain life, than when filtration rate is regulated to maintain constant food intake, as in C. gigas.

According to Bayne & Newell (1983, p. 448), 'in suspension-feeding organisms it is possible to quantify both oxygen consumption and filtration rate synchronously, and thus to arrive at an estimate of the energetic costs of feeding in such animals'. Feeding was found to be associated with a 2-3 fold increase in oxygen consumption compared with the 'standard rate' of the quiescent animal and it was concluded that the overall expenses in water and food processing arise from 'the costs of water transport, filtration, digestion and absorption (including the specific dynamic action of the ration).'

[67]

In *Mytilus californianus* and *Mytilus edulis* they estimated that 24% of an ingested ration of algal cells represented the cost of feeding, of which digestion and assimilation accounted for only 4-6%. These very high costs of water processing were considered as 'sound energetic grounds for the very variable rates of filtration that occur in these and other bivalves, the majority of the energetic costs of activity being eliminated by a reduction of filtration when available ration is insufficient to meet the costs of feeding.' Also Newell & Branch (1980, p. 361) considered cessation of filtration as a means of conservation of energy in filter-feeding bivalves when food resources are scarce.

Several other studies have inferred high energy costs of water processing in bivalves, e.g., in mussels (Bayne & Scullard, 1977; Bayne *et al.*, 1976; Newell & Pye, 1970; Thompson & Bayne, 1972; Widdows, 1973; Winter & Langton, 1976), in oysters (Collier, 1959; Newell *et al.*, 1977), in hard clam (Verduin, 1969), in *Arctica islandica* (Taylor, 1976), and in nine species of bivalves from the eastern coast of Canada (Bernard, 1983). High costs of water processing have also been inferred in other ciliary feeders, including the gastropod *Crepidula fornicata* (Newell & Kofoed, 1977) and the lancelet *Branchiostoma lanceolatum* (Newell, 1970). This concept of energetically costly water processing has been maintained despite evidence that ciliary work is relatively inexpensive and that the energy spent on water processing in filter feeders only represents small fractions of the total metabolism (Clemmesen & Jørgensen, 1987; Famme & Kofoed, 1980; Fenchel, 1980, 1986; Fenchel & Finlay, 1983; Foster-Smith, 1976; Jørgensen, 1955, 1975b, Jørgensen *et al.*, 1986a; Riisgård, 1988b; and above, p. 62). Even filter feeders that pump water by muscular activity maintain low costs in water processing, correlated with low pump pressures as in the ciliary feeders, e.g., *Urechis caupo* (Chapman, 1968) and *Chaetopterus variopedatus* (Brown, 1977; Riisgård, 1989).

The tenacity of life of the belief in high costs of feeding in filter feeders presumably originates in the assumption that increased rates of oxygen consumption with increased pumping rates reflect energetic costs of feeding, and particularly water processing. But as shown in the discussion below of metabolic concepts in filter feeding, this assumption is unwarranted.

In summary, the evidence that has been interpreted in terms of physiological regulation of water processing in filter-feeding bivalves is open to alternative interpretations, consistent with the lack of physiological mechanisms for such regulation. The absence of physiological control of feeding rates in filter-feeding bivalves by control of pumping rates is consistent with the lack of control of respiratory ventilation as a means in the control of the rate of oxygen consumption (Jørgensen *et al.*, 1986a).

CHAPTER XIII

Growth and metabolism
'Scope for growth' and 'growth exploitation'

Growth is an integral component of the matter and energy balance of an organism, as expressed in the familiar equation $I = P + M + E$, where I is ingestion, P is production, M is metabolism and E is excretion, all terms usually being expressed as rates. P stands for somatic growth, reproduction and/or deposition of energy reserves, e.g., glycogen in bivalves. The term E may be subdivided into faeces (F) and urine (U). $P + M$ constitute assimilation (A) and $P + M + U$ matter and/or energy digested and absorbed (see e.g., Grodzinski *et al.*, 1975).

The difference $A - M$ has also been termed 'scope for growth'. This concept was introduced in fish bioenergetics by Warren & Davis (1967), and it has come to play a prominent role in the energetics of filter-feeding bivalves and other invertebrates (Bayne & Newell, 1983; Bayne *et al.*, 1976, 1987, 1989; Gaffney & Diehl, 1986; Thompson & Bayne, 1974; Widdows & Bayne, 1971; Widdows & Johnson, 1988).

'Scope for growth', or net growth efficiency, is, however, a sensitive measure of growth only under conditions far below the optimal. As optimal conditions for growth are approached the 'scope for growth', which increases hyperbolically with assimilation, becomes an increasingly insensitive measure of rates of growth. A term for the exploitation of the potential for growth is therefore needed, particularly in opportunistically feeding and growing animals, such as filter-feeding bivalves. 'Scope for growth' might have been used in the sense of degree of exploitation. But redefinition would lead to confusion, and an alternative expression is to be preferred. The extent to which the inherent potential for growth in a filter-feeding bivalve is being exploited may be termed 'fractional growth exploitation', or shortly 'growth exploitation'.

Expressed in terms of energy, the equation $I = P + M + E$ merely states the constancy of energy, and it tells nothing about physiological or biochemical processes involved or about causal relations between the parameters. But often it is implicitly understood that production (growth) and metabolism are independent, competing processes, for instance in the assumption that the 'scope for growth' can be regulated by adjustments of metabolism (Bayne & Newell, 1983; Buxton *et al.* 1981; Newell *et al.*, 1977). In fact, growth and metabolism are integrated through the energetic costs of growth.

Metabolic concepts in filter feeding

Metabolic rate varies with the functional state of an organism, as reflected in concepts such as basal metabolism, standard metabolism and metabolism of activity. These concepts originated in human and mammalian physiology, and they were subsequently taken over generally by animal physiologists. More recently the concepts have been adopted in a modified form to describe a metabolic pattern believed to characterize filter feeding bivalves and other aquatic invertebrates. The 'standard rate' of metabolism is the oxygen uptake during quiescence, and the 'active rate' the uptake at maximal activity. Between these two rates are a variety of 'routine rates' corresponding to various activity levels (Newell, 1970). Applied on a filter-feeding bivalve, *Mytilus edulis*, the 'standard rate' is the rate of oxygen uptake in animals with open valves and partially extruding mantle edges but showing minimal filtration activity in the absence of particulate food, whereas the 'active rate' is the rate of oxygen uptake in fed animals filtering at a maximum rate (Thompson & Bayne, 1972). Between these two extremes 'routine rates' intervene, and are correlated with corresponding filtration rates (Bayne, Thompson & Widdows, 1976).

The definitions of 'standard', 'routine' and 'active'' metabolic rates in filter-feeding bivalves are based on the above-mentioned assumption that oxygen consumption reflects energetic costs of water processing and feeding, and that these energetic costs can be physiologically regulated. As mentioned, this assumption is unwarranted. In mussels, oxygen is taken up by diffusion through the epithelium lining the mantle cavity, the gills being of marginal importance in the overall oxygen consumption (Famme & Kofoed, 1980). The flow through the mantle cavity is laminar and the rate of oxygen uptake is determined by diffusion through boundary layers (Jørgensen et al., 1986a), as well as through the tissues of the body, transport via the blood circulation being slight (Booth & Mangum, 1979) or insignificant (Famme, 1981). This physically determined oxygen consumption is sensitive to the flow rate through the mantle cavity, which determines the thickness of the boundary layer and thus the diffusional constraints on the uptake. The relation between oxygen consumption and flow rate is hyperbolic, and consumption approximates independence of flow rate when the pump capacity is approached.

The low rate of oxygen consumption that prevails in mussels with reduced valve gape in particle-depleted water thus does not reflect physiological regulation, such as a 'standard' metabolism saving energetic costs of water processing, but is a consequence of increasing diffusional resistance with decreasing flow through the mantle cavity.

The lack of physiological reality in the concepts of 'standard', 'routine' and 'active' metabolic rates, as adopted to filter-feeding bivalves, is also evident from the fact that oxygen uptake increases steeply with water processing only at low rates of filtration, typical of adverse conditions. The concepts are therefore irrelevant to unrestrained water processing.

An interpretation of the correlation between oxygen consumption and filtration rate in mussels with reduced gaping of the valves in terms of energetic costs of activity is illfounded also because a filter-feeding bivalve that reduces the valve gape and retracts mantle edges and siphons is presumably more 'active' than it is in the fully open and relaxed state, even though the muscular activity involved in contraction of the adductor muscles and retraction of the mantle edges and siphons is energetically inexpensive, due to a particular molluscan type of muscular activity. This is the catch mechanism, which maintains the contracted state without expenditure of energy until it is relaxed through nervous activity, involving serotonin and catch-relaxing peptide (Hirata et al., 1989a, b; Muneoka & Kamura, 1982; Twarog, 1967; York & Twarog, 1973).

The reduced aerobic metabolism correlated with reduced gaping or closure of the valves in the absence of food and other particles is not compensated by an increased anaerobic metabolism (Famme et al., 1981). The behavioural response of filter-feeding bivalves to depletion of suspended par-

[71]

ticles in the ambient water thus reduces the total energy expenditure of the organism in the absence of food, and the behaviour may be interpreted as an energy-saving adaptation or as an exaptation.

The physiological analysis of relations between metabolism and filtration and feeding should be made in animals under optimal conditions, where water is processed at rates that correspond to the capacity of the pump. Under such conditions the musculature is relaxed and motoric activity may be represented primarily by the cilia responsible for the processing of the water, the work done being independent of particles suspended in the water.

Recently, Widdows & Hawkins (1989) concluded from the absence of any measurable increment in heat dissipation rate in *Mytilus edulis* in response to addition of inert particles to the ambient water that the mechanical component of food acquisition appears to be minimal. This conclusion is unwarranted because it erroneously implies that the activity of the lateral cilia depends upon the presence of suspended food or other particles.

Energetic costs of growth

Given that the mechanical work done is independent of the feeding rate the relationship between growth and metabolism can be ascertained by feeding at various levels. This approach has been successfully applied in a number of ectothermic animals belonging to several taxonomic groups and various ontogenetic stages, including copepods (Kiørboe *et al.*, 1985), fish (Jobling, 1983, 1985; Kiørboe & Møhlenberg, 1987; Kiørboe *et al.*, 1987) and toads (Jørgensen, 1988).

Data on the relationship between rates of metabolism, M, and growth, G, are also available for mussels, *Mytilus edulis* (Kiørboe *et al.*, 1981). The relationship could be described as a linear function $M = 0.024 + 0.29G$, where M and G are expressed in mg organic matter per mg organic body mass per day (Figure 27). The initial dry body mass of the mussels was about 20-25 mg.

Recent experiments by Hawkins *et al.* (1989) and Widdows & Hawkins (1989) corroborate and extend the analysis of the energetic costs of feeding, growth and biosynthesis in young mussels. The relationship between total metabolic rate and growth, expressed in J d^{-1} per 10 mg dry mass could be described by $M = 3.50 + 0.29G$.

[72]

The intersection with the ordinate is the metabolic rate at zero growth, that is, cost of maintenance, whereas the slope of the regression reflects energetic costs of growth + increased costs of maintenance that arise with the increase in body mass. Corrections were made for costs of maintenance according to Jørgensen (1988), and the relation between metabolic costs of growth M_G and growth could be described by the linear function $M_G = -0.00009 + 0.20G$ (Figure 27). It is thus indicated that the physiological costs of growth amounts to $(0.2/1.2) \cdot 100 = 17\%$ of matter and energy assimilated in excess of energetic costs of maintenance. At the highest growth rate in the experiment the energetic cost of growth approached half the total metabolic expenditure. As shown below (p. 78) the fastest growing mussels were close to fully exploiting their potential for growth.

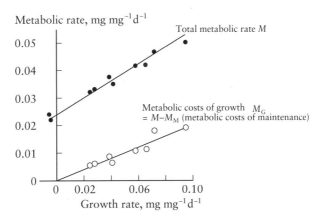

Figure 27. *Mytilus edulis.* Relation between mass specific growth (G) and metabolic rates (Based on data from Kiørboe *et al.*, 1981).

Kiørboe (1988) recalculated the data from Kiørboe *et al.* (1981) by plotting growth rate on assimilation rate A. The regression was $G = -0.027 + 0.91A$. This slope thus indicated that about 90% of assimilated matter and energy in excess of maintenance requirement was deposited as growth. Calculations showed that the physiological costs of growth of about 10% equalled the theoretical, biochemical costs of biosynthesis. These costs were dominated by synthesis of protein, and they left no space for growth-dependent increase in protein turnover. This conclusion is consistent with the findings of Hawkins *et al.* (1989) that the rate of protein degradation in young mussels is independent of growth rate, that is, protein synthesis.

In mussels and other sessile filter-feeding bivalves we may thus distinguish between metabolic costs of maintenance and metabolic costs of

[73]

growth which reflects rates of growth. At maximum rates of growth the metabolic costs incured may constitute a substantial proportion of the total metabolism. Also within a bioenergetic framework the important parameter to
analyse in filter-feeding bivalves is therefore the potential for growth and
factors affecting its exploitation.

Growth potential

The potential for growth (production) may be expressed as the maximum
growth rate, μ_{max}, or as the maximum growth efficiency. The instantaneous,
specific growth rate μ is calculated as $\ln(W_t/W_0)t^{-1}$, where W_t is body mass
at time t and W_0 is body mass at zero time. The growth efficiency is defined
as the ratio growth/ingestion, the gross growth efficiency K_1, or as the ratio
growth/assimilation, the net growth efficiency K_2 (Ivlev, 1945). Growth
efficiencies are thus derived from the equation $I = P + M + E$.

K_2 is related to the specific growth rate μ according to $K_2 = \mu/(\mu + M)$,
where M is the mass specific metabolic rate. The term M encompasses
metabolic cost of maintenance of the organism, M_M, as well as metabolic
cost of growth, M_G. Thus $K_2 = \mu/(\mu + M_M + M_G)$. If M_G is proportional to
μ, $K_2 = \mu/(a\mu + M_M)$, where $a > 1$. K_2 increases with μ and reaches maximum at μ_{max}.

The relationship between growth rate and net growth efficiency in
young mussels, *Mytilus edulis*, is shown in Figure 28. The data are based
upon measurements made both in the laboratory (Kiørboe *et al.*, 1981;

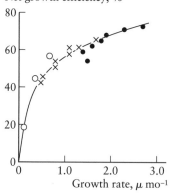

Net growth efficiency, %

Figure 28. *Mytilus edulis*. Relation between mass
specific growth rate (μ mo^{-1}) and net growth efficiency, based on data from:

× Kiørboe *et al.*, 1981,
● Riisgård & Poulsen, 1981,
○ Riisgård & Randløv, 1981.

Growth rate, μ mo^{-1}

[74]

Riisgård & Randløv, 1981) and in the field (Riisgård & Poulsen, 1981). It may be seen that μ_{max} approaches a value of about 3 mo^{-1}, whereas K_2 asymptotically approaches values of about 75%. Net growth efficiencies at this level are typical of mussels during the productive seasons of the year (Jørgensen, 1976b). It is noteworthy that the potential for growth may be far from fully exploited even at relatively high growth efficiencies. At a net growth efficiency of 50%, corresponding to about $2/3$ of the maximum efficiency, only about $1/5$ of the potential for growth was exploited (Figure 28). Under optimal conditions mussels maintain constant, high growth efficiencies from larval to adult stages (Jørgensen, 1952, 1976b).

Figure 29. *Mytilus edulis*. Mass specific growth rates (μ d^{-1}) as a function of size (g tissue dry mass). The lines indicate calculated values, the points values measured in the laboratory (filled symbols) or in nature (open symbols). Inserted figures are values of the exponent b in the relation $M = aW^{(b-1)}$ (from Hamburger *et al.*, 1983).

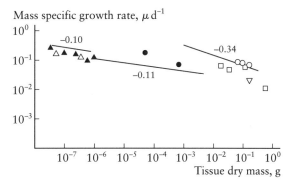

Also the potential for growth remains high. Hamburger *et al.* (1983) calculated the mass specific growth rate μ from the equation $\mu = K_2 M/(1 - K_2)W$, where W is the body mass, at masses that spanned seven orders of magnitude. The results, together with data they collected from the literature, are shown in Figure 29. Growth potentials corresponding to 0.1 d^{-1}, or about 3 mo^{-1}, are maintained to adult stages. It may be noted that the calculated data have negative slopes that can be shown to vary with the exponent b in the relation $M = aW^b$.

$$\mu = \frac{K_2}{1 - K_2}\, aW^b/W = \frac{K_2}{1 - K_2}\, aW^{(b-1)}.$$

Thus, when $b \to 1$, $\mu \to \dfrac{K_2}{1 - K_2}\, a$,

that is, constant, independent of body mass. At $b < 1$, μ decreases with increasing body mass.

A constant instantaneous growth rate μ at increasing body mass thus depends upon a linear relationship between body mass and metabolic rate, that is, $b = 1$ in the allometric relation $M = aW^b$. In contrast, a constant net growth efficiency K_2 with increasing body mass merely depends upon the values of b being identical in the allometric relations between body mass and rates of metabolism as well as water processing. At values of $b < 1$ the components of mass specific metabolism M, i.e., costs of maintenance M_M and growth M_G, decrease in parallel with increasing body mass, maintaining the growth efficiency constant.

Most investigations on growth in filter-feeding bivalves aim at estimating growth efficiencies from measurements of ingestion rates and metabolic rates, where ingestion rates are calculated from filtration rates and concentrations of accessible food in the ambient water. Rates of metabolism M and of filtration F can both be related to body mass according to the equations $M = a_M W^{b_M}$ and $F = a_F W^{b_F}$. The relative values of the exponents in these two equations will affect the growth efficiency as a function of body mass W. Thus, K_2 decreases with increasing W if $b_M > b_F$, whereas a constant K_2 implies that $b_M = b_F$.

The coefficients a_M and a_F and the exponents b_M and b_F at μ_{max} $(= K_{2\,max})$ may therefore be used to assess deviations of experimentally obtained values from values applying at conditions compatible with full exploitation of the potential for growth of the animals. In making such assessments the unit mass should be chosen close to the mean of the experimental animals in order to minimize the distorting effects of the mathematical interdependence between a and b (Gould, 1966).

Most investigators have found high values, about 0.6-0.7, for both exponents, b_F tending to be slightly lower than b_M (reviewed by Winter, 1978; Bayne & Newell, 1983). In studies where filtration rates are measured by the flow technique as used by Walne (1972) and by Bayne and his coworkers (Bayne *et al.*, 1977; Thompson & Bayne, 1972) this difference was more pronounced, with b_F values < 0.5. Thus, in *Mytilus edulis*, the mean value of b_F was 0.38, ranging from 0.025-0.51 (Widdows, 1978). In *Mytilus californianus*, b_F was found to be 0.42 in starved mussels and 0.46 in fed (Bayne *et al.*, 1976).

Values of b_F lower than of b_M may result from the increasing sensitivity towards adverse environmental conditions, including high algal concentrations, with increasing size of the animals (Jørgensen, 1949; Sanina, 1976).

[76]

Such a relation will tend to reduce the values of both b_M and b_F, but b_F will be more affected than b_M, because the effects of a reduced rate of ventilation on oxygen consumption may be more or less compensated by an increased extraction of oxygen from the water passing the mantle cavity (Jørgensen *et al.*, 1986a). The very low values, less than 0.5, may also be of technical nature, inherent in the geometry and flow rate through the experimental chamber (Hildreth & Crisp, 1976; Riisgård, 1977).

The literature does include reports on net growth efficiencies in filter-feeding bivalves that decline with increasing size. These data, obtained in the laboratory, should therefore be discussed in the light of the finding of potentially constant efficiencies in nature (Jørgensen, 1976b).

In *Mytilus edulis*, ranging in body mass from 0.1-2 g dry body mass and fed cultures of the flagellate *Tetraselmis suecica* at concentrations of 0.5-20 cells μl^{-1}, or 0.033-1.32 mg dry matter l^{-1}, Thompson & Bayne (1974) found the maximal net growth efficiency to decline from 0.75 in 0.1 g mussels fed algae at a concentration of about 1 mg l^{-1} to −0.02 in 2 g mussels. The growth efficiencies were calculated as (assimilation − metabolism)/assimilation. These growth efficiencies thus indicated that the large mussels were in negative energy balance independently of the concentration of food. The declining growth efficiencies presumably resulted from clearances that decreased with increasing body mass. From the relation between filtration rates and body mass in mussels under optimal conditions (Table 10, p. 86) it can be estimated that in the experiments of Thompson & Bayne (1974) the 0.1 g mussels cleared the algal suspensions at about 50 % of their capacity, decreasing to < 20 % in the 2 g mussels. The results are thus inconclusive in ecological terms.

Data that indicate declining growth efficiency with increasing body size are also available for the oyster *Ostrea edulis*. Buxton *et al.* (1981) established energy budgets for oyster spat of about 5 mg dry body mass. From their data on assimilated energy and 'scope for growth' it can be seen that the net growth efficiencies are high, reaching a value of 96 %. Such unrealistically high growth efficiencies presumably arose from methodological errors in the determinations of assimilation efficiencies. The efficiency was calculated under the assumption that inorganic matter ingested with the food equalled that egested with the faeces (Conover, 1966). The method requires that the food contains substantial amounts of non-absorbable inorganic constituents, which does not apply to the cultures of *Tetraselmis suecica* used as food. (The same criticism can be raised against the paper by Thompson & Bayne (1974) in which assimilation efficiencies were likewise determined according to Conover).

Buxton *et al.* (1981) inferred that the net growth efficiency declined with body size by referring to Newell *et al.* (1977) who found that about 300 mg oysters cleared suspensions of the diatom *Phaeodactylum tricornutum* at low rates compared with the rates of oxygen consumption. From the data given in Table 10 it can, however, be estimated that the large oysters processed the water at only about 3 % of the pump capacity at the acclimation temperature of 15 °C and about 20 % at the acclimation temperature of 20 °C (Table 1, in Newell *et al.*, 1977). In contrast, the oyster spat in Buxton *et al.*'s (1981) experiments utilized the full capacity, the clearance amounting to $30 \, l \, g^{-1} \, h^{-1}$, to be compared with the calculated value of $28 \, l \, g^{-1} \, h^{-1}$. Again the data disclose effects of experimental conditions rather than of any inherent relationship between body size and growth efficiency in oysters.

CHAPTER XIV

Ecophysiological aspects

Exploitation of growth potential in mussels

The mussel *Mytilus edulis* is the only filter-feeding bivalve the growth of which has been extensively investigated, as a prerequisite to assessment of the growth potential and its exploitation in nature as well as in the laboratory. Most studies of growth in nature are based on measurements of increases in shell length. It is therefore important to know the relations between growth in length and in body mass. Such relations may vary with the level of food in the ambient water and at decreasing food levels shell growth may even continue after growth in body mass has become negative (Kiørboe *et al.*, 1981; Riisgård & Randløv, 1981). However, at optimal food levels growth in mass and net growth efficiency may be highly correlated with growth in length, as shown in Figure 30. The relationship depicted is based on growth in young mussels transplanted to various localities in the Limfjord, Denmark, in the month of July when the concentrations of phy-

[*78*]

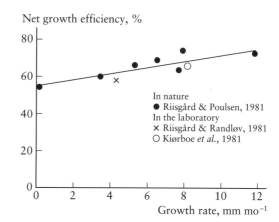

Figure 30. *Mytilus edulis*. Relation between growth rate and net growth efficiency at high food levels in nature and in the laboratory.

toplankton were high and growth was not food-limited (Riisgård & Poulsen, 1981). The low linear growth rates were found in localities close to areas with oxygen depletion in bottom waters. It is noteworthy that at high food levels growth in length is a much more sensitive measure of 'quality' of the environment than is growth efficiency.

It is thus indicated that at optimal conditions for growth, when net growth efficiencies amount to 60-70 %, growth in shell length may approach 10 mm mo^{-1}. Growth rates of this order have been recorded in nature on localities geographically distributed from Europe to North America and ranging in latitude from California to Alaska (Table 8).

Most of the data in Table 8 are obtained from mussels attached to suspended ropes or net bags, as used in the culture of natural populations of mussels. These conditions minimize exposure to water that has been depleted of food particles by neighbouring mussels. Mussels suspended in the water column grow faster and more synchronously than mussels on the natural beds (Bøhle, 1970; Fréchette & Bourget, 1985b; Rodhouse *et al.*, 1984).

Mussels that grow 7-11 mm mo^{-1} presumably more or less fully exploit their potential for growth. But populations of *Mytilus edulis* often, or perhaps mostly, grow slower than their inherent potential. Thus, growth is relatively slow in populations of mussels on exposed rocky shores (Harger, 1970; Seed, 1968, 1969). Also exposure to air in mussels inhabiting the intertidal zone strongly affects growth, and the growth rate decreases rapidly with increased duration of exposure (Baird, 1966; Coulthard, 1929; Seed, 1969; Warren, 1936). Baird (1966) extrapolated growth to be zero at 56 % exposure.

[79]

Table 8. *Mytilus edulis*. Growth rates of shells recorded in nature and in the laboratory.

FIELD DATA		Mean growth rate,	
Locality	Season	mm mo^{-1}	Reference
Limfjord, Denmark	July	7-11	Riisgård & Poulsen, 1981
Oslo fjord, Norway	Aug.-Sep.	10	Bøhle, 1970
Morecamb Bay, England	May-Aug.	8	Dare, 1973 (cit. Kiørboe *et al.*, 1981)
Killary Harbour, Ireland	June-July	7	Rodhouse *et al.*, 1984
Liune Mhiurich, Scotland	July-Nov.	8	Mason, 1969 (cit. Kiørboe *et al.*, 1981)
Ria de Vigo, Spain	June-Sep.	9	Mason, 1976
Alamitos Bay, California	Whole year	9	Reich, 1964
Southern coast of Alaska	June-Aug.	7	Paul *et al.*, 1978
LABORATORY DATA Algal species	Algal conc. mg dry wt l^{-1}		
Dunaliella, Isochrysis	2.3 *	1.5	Winter, 1974
Dunaliella	3.2 *	0.9	Winter, 1976; Winter & Langton, 1976
Chaetoceros, Phaeodactylum ca.16 *		0.2	Tenore *et al.*, 1973
Phaeodactylum	0.05	4.8	Riisgård & Randløv, 1981
Phaeodactylum	0.33	5.8	Kiørboe *et al.*, 1981
Phaeodactylum + 8 mg silt l^{-1}	0.24	7.2	– –

* Daily ration per mussel

The sensitivity of growth towards environmental factors is also evident from the tendency of mussels to grow at low rates when placed in wire trays or boxes (Baird, 1966; Coulthard, 1929; Lande, 1973; Warren 1936). The plasticity of growth in mussels is revealed by the fact that small and old, non-growing mussels from the high shore tidal level renew linear growth when transplanted sublittorally (Seed, 1968), even though the growth rate of young mussels may not be fully restored (Baird, 1966).

These observations on growth of *M. edulis* in nature may be compared with results obtained in the laboratory. Table 8 shows that in the laboratory, mussels mostly grew only slowly even at high concentrations of algae in the ambient water. Only in the experiments of Kiørboe *et al.* (1981) and Riisgård & Randløv (1981) did growth reach or approach that pertaining under optimal conditions in nature. In these experiments the mussels were fed a culture of the diatom *Phaeodactylum tricornutum* at natural concentrations. Experiments were made on groups of mussels over periods of two to several weeks. Experiments were made in winter, spring and summer, with no obvious seasonal effect on growth and growth efficiency.

Kiørboe *et al.* (1981) found that addition of silt at a concentration of about 5 mg l^{-1} increased growth rate, and the net growth efficiency reached a maximum of 65 % at an algal concentration of about 0.3 mg dry matter l^{-1}. Also in *Spisula subtruncata* did addition of silt, in concentrations up to 20-30 mg l^{-1}, increase growth rate and net growth efficiencies. In *M. edulis*, the silt acted both by increasing rates of water pumping and efficiency of assimilation of the ingested algae, whereas in *S. subtruncata* only assimilation increased (Møhlenberg & Kiørboe, 1981). By contrast, addition of silt in amounts up to 25 mg l^{-1} to an algal diet of *Pseudoisochrysis paradoxa* did not affect growth rates in optimally growing hard clams, *Mercenaria mercenaria*, whereas growth rates were reduced at a concentration of 44 mg l^{-1} (Bricelj *et al.*, 1984). High concentrations of silt and other suspended matter in the water are probably deleterious to growth in filter-feeding animals generally, including bivalves. But the levels at which adverse effects are reached presumably vary between species and even between populations of the same species, correlated with the normal loads of suspended matter in the habitat (Bricelj *et al.*, 1984; Kiørboe *et al.*, 1980; Robinson *et al.*, 1984; Theisen, 1982).

It may be concluded that both in nature and in the laboratory exploitation of the potential for growth depends upon optimal conditions applying during the productive seasons of the year. It is noteworthy that optimal conditions for growth in the laboratory might include the presence of silt at a concentration that was an order of magnitude or more higher than that of food particles, whereas maximum growth rates were not obtained by feeding with algal cultures at concentrations above a normal range (Table 8).

At a growth rate in the laboratory of about 7 mm mo^{-1} and a net growth efficiency of 65 %, the mussels, of an initial body mass of 20-25 mg, processed on an average 0.96 l h^{-1} of the ambient water during the 13 days the experiment lasted (Kiørboe *et al.*, 1981). This may be compared with the rate of 0.74 l h^{-1} predicted from the relation between body mass and clearance found by Møhlenberg & Riisgård (1979) (Table 10, p. 86). The low growth rates at high concentrations of algae indicate that water processing was depressed by a greater amount than that corresponding to compensation associated with increased food levels.

[*81*]

These findings underline the difficulties in establishing conditions in the laboratory that permit full relaxation of adductor muscles and extension of the mantle edges and siphon required for the full use of the pump capacity. Even the rates of water transport measured in the laboratory in undisturbed bivalves exposed to natural concentrations of algal suspension presumably tend to be lower than those prevailing under optimal conditions in nature.

Mussels do exploit their potential for growth when the ambient water contains concentrations of algae and silt typical of the season of high productivity. Such exploitation depends upon constant water processing, corresponding to the capacity of the pump. This conclusion is consistent with the statement by Bayne & Newell (1983, p. 487) that 'it appears that suspension-feeding bivalves in the natural habitat may normally function at food concentrations for which growth efficiency is a rapidly increasing function of food availability'. However, food does presumably approach concentrations compatible with maximum growth rate during the productive season. There is no clear evidence for a seasonal variation in growth potential. This agrees with the finding that mussels process water at rates that vary with the temperature rather than with the season (Jørgensen, 1975a; Jørgensen et al., 1986b, 1988, 1990).

Ecophysiological implications

This 'ecological conception' of feeding in mussels leaves no space for physiological regulation of the rates of water processing according to levels of food concentrations or to endogenously determined seasonal cycles, as assumed, e.g., by Hawkins and his coworkers (Hawkins & Bayne, 1984, 1985; Hawkins et al., 1983, 1985).

Hawkins et al. advanced hypotheses according to which feeding, metabolism and growth (production) constitute controlled processes, based on endogenous rhythms that are correlated with the seasons. The hypotheses further elaborate ideas evolved by Bayne and Newell and their coworkers over the last decades (see Bayne & Newell, 1983). It is therefore pertinent to evaluate the evidence on which these hypotheses are based.

Hawkins and coworkers determined food ingestion from the rate at which the mussels cleared the ambient water of *Phaeodactylum tricornutum* cells, and food absorption was determined from the efficiency with which

[82]

the algae were digested and absorbed. The proportion of food metabolized was determined from the rate of oxygen consumption and excretion of nitrogen. From these data, expressed in terms of energy equivalents, the energy balance of the mussels could be computed. Such computations were made in three experiments on mussels collected in March, June and October and acclimated to the laboratory conditions for 5-6 weeks. The actual feeding experiments lasted 6 hours. During these 6 hours the energy balance was positive only in the June-July experiment, when the net growth efficiency was calculated to be 25 % (Table 9), corresponding to about $1/10$ of the potential for growth in young mussels (Figure 28, p. 74).

Table 9. *Mytilus edulis.* Net growth efficiencies, K_2, in mussels fed *Phaeodactylum tricornutum.*

Algal concentration		Tem-pera-ture, °C	K_2	Date	Duration of experiment	Reference
org. matter mg l^{-1}	cells ml^{-1} $\times 10^{-3}$					
0.11	6.9±2.9	13	0.43	April-	19 d	Kiørboe *et al.*, 1981
0.19	11.8±4.5	13	0.51	June	20 d	
0.051	3.0±1.5	15	0.19	January	24 d	Riisgård & Randløv, 1981
0.051	3.0±1.4	15	0.45	March	47 d	
		9	−0.65	March*		
	5-10	13	0.25	June	6 h	Hawkins *et al.*, 1985
		13	−0.13	October		

*Month of collection, actual experiments after 5 to 6 week periods of acclimation.

These results may be compared with those obtained in the above-mentioned long-term experiments in which the mussels were also fed *Phaeodactylum tricornutum* at low to medium concentrations. Table 9 shows that in these experiments, which lasted 3-7 weeks, growth was always positive independently of the time of the year from January to June and even at a mean concentration of algae as low as 3000 cells ml^{-1}. There is thus no indication of an endogenous seasonal rhythm in rates of feeding and energy utilization in mussels kept under conditions that are compatible with the use of the full capacity for water processing. This conclusion is further substantiated by the demonstration that cold temperate zone mussels may in fact grow during winter.

[83]

Møhlenberg & Andersen (1987) followed the rate of growth in young mussels from October to December at various stations inside the harbour of Copenhagen, Denmark, as well as at one station just outside the harbour. The mussels were placed in net bags 2 m above the bottom. During the period from 22 October to 12 November the mussels increased in body mass at all stations, at mean growth rates μ that often exceeded 0.02 d^{-1}, corresponding to about $^1/_5$ of the potential for growth under optimal conditions (Figure 28). During the period 12 November to 4 December, growth stagnated, and was at some stations even negative, except outside the harbour where the rate of growth amounted to 0.01 d^{-1} or about $^1/_{10}$ the potential. The positive growth at the station outside the harbour was correlated with a higher concentration of chlorophyll a in the water at this station than at those inside the harbour area. During the last period from 4-17 December growth was negative at most stations inside the harbour and zero at the remaining inside stations as well as at the station outside the harbour. This pattern of growth correlated well with the steady decline in chlorophyll a concentrations from about 1.1 µg l^{-1} to about 0.7 µg l^{-1} during the experimental period of 8 weeks. Concurrently, the temperature declined from about 10 °C to 7 °C.

The low or even negative energy balances obtaining in the experiments of Hawkins *et al.* (1985) may be explained by the algal clearances measured, which corresponded to only about half of the rates at which optimally filtering mussels have been found to clear the water (Table 10, p. 86). The data on which Hawkins *et al.* base their hypotheses thus presumably refer to particular experimental conditions that do not warrant ecological interpretations. The same applies to some other studies on feeding and bioenergetics in mussels (Bayne & Widdows, 1978; Bayne *et al.*, 1987, 1989; Lucas *et al.*, 1987; Widdows & Johnson, 1988; Widdows *et al.*, 1984).

The experimental data available are thus not necessarily in conflict with the concept that under optimal conditions in nature or in the laboratory mussels process water at the full capacity of the pump. Feeding rates under such conditions depend upon the concentration of food particles suspended in the ambient water. Patterns of growth and/or production of gametes are adapted to seasonally varying food availability, and growth may accordingly vary seasonally from positive during periods of high phytoplankton production and temperature to negative at low phytoplankton production and temperature. In their ability to survive at a variety of growth rates and to withstand many months of near starvation during the seasons of low productivity and temperature, mussels adhere to the pattern that may apply generally for sedentary suspension feeders inhabiting higher latitudes (Crisp, 1964).

Optimal foraging theory and filter feeding

In ecology optimal foraging theory has met with some success in interpreting feeding behaviour (Hughes, 1990; Pyke, 1984). The theory basically applies to macrophagous animals that can choose among individual food items and regulate feeding activity. The theory therefore seems unrealistic for microphages, such as filter feeders. However, Taghon (1981) developed a model for microphages based on alteration in ingestion rate as a mechanism for optimizing net rate of energy gain. This model has been adopted for filter-feeding bivalves (Bayne, 1987; Bayne et al., 1988). The model expresses the net rate of energy gain, E_n, as the difference between rates of assimilation and metabolism, the 'scope for growth' concept, in the form

$$E_n = C \cdot A_e \cdot E_f - k_1 \cdot C^x ,$$

where C is consumption (ingestion) rate, A_e is absorption efficiency and E_f is the nutritional value of the food; k_1 and x are parameters which relate the rate of consumption to associated energy costs.

The model has been used to simulate a variety of physiological adaptations and adjustments to environmental factors, serving to maximize net energy gain in intertidal mussels (Bayne et al., 1988). The simulation implies that mussels are capable of regulating ingestion rates by controlling the filtration rate both according to quantity and quality (food value) of suspended food particles in the water. As argued above, these implications are unwarranted, and optimal foraging theory seems physiologically irrelevant to feeding in filter-feeding bivalves.

Pump capacities

The pump capacity is the basic bioenergetic parameter in filter-feeding bivalves but data on such capacities are scarce. This may be due to the difficulties in establishing experimental conditions under which the bivalves pro-

[85]

cess the ambient water according to the inherent capacity of the pump, but also to a lacking awareness among investigators of the importance of establishing such references for the assessment of their experimental data.

In recent years, however, attempts have been made to determine pump capacities and their relation to body size in a number of filter-feeding bivalves. Some relations are presented in Table 10, expressed by the regression constants of pumping rates on body mass. The values of Møhlenberg & Riisgård (1979) and Riisgård (1988a) are based on rates at which undisturbed bivalves, collected in Danish waters and coastal water off Georgia, USA, cleared unicellular algae suspended at natural concentrations in the water. The values of Meyhöfer (1985) are pumping rates measured with a thermistor microflowmeter in bivalves collected around San Juan Island, Washington, USA. Also Coughlan & Ansell (1964) used a flowmeter to determine pumping rates in undisturbed clams that had established themselves in sand.

The similarity in rates of water processing in filter-feeding bivalves belonging to the same biotope, or to biotopes with comparable productivity,

Table 10. Pump capacities in filter-feeding bivalves: Constants in the allometric relation, filtration rate $(l\ h^{-1}) = aW(g\ dry\ flesh\ weight)^b$.

Species	W, g	n	a	b	r
Cardium echinatum*	0.080-2.13	10	4.2	0.62	0.99
Clinocardium nuttalii**	2.47 -4.46	5	3.1	0.80	0.96
Venus (Mercenaria) mercenaria****					
Typical rate	0.36 -4.81	12	2.6	0.74	0.95
Maximum rate		9	2.7	0.76	0.96
Mytilus edulis*	0.011-1.36	6	7.5	0.66	0.99
Veligers and postmetamorphic	0.05 -10 mg	14	25	1.03	0.99
Mytilus californianus**	0.98 -8.66	4	7.9	0.72	0.99
Modiolus modiolus*	0.058-1.56	7	6.0	0.75	0.98
Geukensia (Modiolus) demissa***	0.009-1.04	18	6.2	0.83	0.95
Arctica islandica*	0.011-1.31	7	5.6	0.62	0.99
Crassostrea virginica***	0.063-0.99	10	6.8	0.73	0.76
Chlamys hastata**	1.75 -2.23	4	8.6	0.94	1.00

*   Møhlenberg & Riisgård, 1979; Riisgård et al., 1980;
**   Meyhöfer, 1985;
***   Riisgård, 1988a;
**** Coughlan & Ansell, 1964.

suggests that the sets of reference values in Table 10 may also be used to assess the ecological relevance of experimental data obtained in other species from similar biotopes.

The pumping rates recorded in Table 10 were measured at the temperature typical of the season of growth, e.g., 13 °C in Denmark and 27 °C in Georgia. Such adaptation of filtration rates to temperature was also found between populations of *Mytilus californianus* from various localities along the west coast of USA, ranging from Friday Harbour to Los Angeles (Rao, 1953). Temperature adaptation of filtration (feeding) rates is presumably integrated with other bioenergetic rate functions, such as the metabolic rate (Bullock, 1955; Thorson, 1936, 1952), thus maintaining a potential for growth that is relatively independent of latitude (Table 8, p. 80).

The finding of similar rates of water processing in bivalve species from the west coast and east coast of USA and northern Europe agrees with all localities representing coastal habitats with comparable productivity, as reflected in the prevailing concentrations of food. The finding of similar rates in species belonging to different taxonomic groups and ecological types support the concept that these rates constitute fixed adaptations. The concept is also consistent with the finding of lower filtration rates in freshwater bivalves (Kryger & Riisgård, 1988).

CHAPTER XV

Hierarchical analysis of filter feeding

Evolution of automatized water processing in filter-feeding bivalves of capacities dimensioned for optimal growth during the productive seasons of the year renders control of feeding rates irrelevant and thus explains the absence of physiological mechanisms for such control. It is therefore of interest to understand how ideas about complex physiological regulation arose. A main factor seems to be the absence of hierarchical thinking, implying functional analysis that includes organizational levels below that in focus and interpretation of experimental data within a framework defined by the level above.

[*87*]

The importance of introducing higher levels in order to understand events at the levels below has been recognized repeatedly by scientists representing all levels and branches from physics over molecular biology, genetics, physiology, general biology to behaviour, evolution, ecology and sociology (Dobzhansky, 1941; Dubos, 1965; Goldstein, 1939; Jacob, 1976; Lashley, 1929; Mayr, 1982; Medawar, 1967; Novikoff, 1945; Pianka, 1978; Prosser, 1965; Rothchild, 1979; Schneirla, 1941; Woodger, 1930-31). Still, these recognitions have appeared isolated and sporadic, of little general consequence.

In contemporary biology organizational level concepts mainly appear in more or less profitable debates under the heading of reductionism versus holism, or equivalent terms (Ayala & Dobzhansky, 1974; Dunbar, 1980; Gould & Lewontin, 1979; Koestler & Smythies, 1969; Larkin, 1977). Concurrently with these debates, tools for the analysis within the framework of organizational levels are, however, being developed within the discipline of hierarchy theory, particularly by philosophers, but also by persons with other professional backgrounds (Conrad, 1976, 1983; Feibleman, 1954-55; Halfon, 1979; Pattee, 1970, 1973; Simon, 1962; Whitehead, 1926 (1985); Whyte *et al.*, 1969; Woodger, 1930-31). So far this development has passed unnoticed, or unappreciated, by most practising biologists, except perhaps among those representing the highest levels of organization, ecology and evolution theory. It may be no incidence that the usefulness of the concept of organizational, or integrative, levels has particularly been realized by practitioners at the highest levels of biology, where the need may be felt more strongly than at the lower levels. In the eighties two treatises have appeared that specifically develop ecological and evolutionary hierarchy theory (Allen & Starr, 1982; Salthe, 1985), whereas physiology largely has remained immune to epistemological thinking.

Filter feeding in bivalves offers a good example of the importance of hierarchical analysis in biological explanation in order to avoid fallacious *ad hoc* interpretations of experimental data. In physiological studies of bivalve filter feeding the focal level is the organism, including the filter pump, and the level of interpretation is the organism (population)–environment entity. These are the fundamental levels of organization at which the ecological physiologist operates (Jørgensen, 1983c, 1990b).

At the population–environment level the capacity of water processing, that is, rates of water pumping and efficiencies of filtration, are adapted to the productivity of the environment (Jørgensen, 1966, 1975b; Riisgård,

1990). The concentrations of phytoplankton thus constitute the primary boundary conditions in determining the water-processing capacity of the filter feeders inhabiting the environment.

In the temperate zone, the seasonally fluctuating food levels act as an additional boundary condition. At higher latitudes, fluctuations in food, and perhaps also in temperature, may even impose alternating periods of positive and negative energy balances on the populations of filter-feeding bivalves. The population response is cyclic growth and storage of energy to cover deficits for maintenance during seasons of low productivity. In some filter-feeding bivalves, such as *Mytilus edulis*, matter stored may be used not only for maintenance, but also for production of gametes during periods of negative food balance.

The relationships established between filter-feeding bivalves and their environments are characterized by adaptedness combined with high adaptability, where the adaptedness refers to fixed adaptations that fit the population to its environment and adaptability is the ability to cope with the uncertainty of this environment (Conrad, 1976, 1983; Salthe, 1985). The adaptability is reflected in the opportunistic exploitation of potentials for production (somatic growth, reproduction and storage), which is characteristic of temperate zone bivalves and which allows mussels and other bivalves to invade habitats, such as the tidal zone, that are prohibitive for the full exploitation of the growth potential. Also the habit of settling in dense beds is incompatible with such exploitation by all members of the bed.

In organisms that exhibit such highly plastic and opportunistic patterns of feeding and growth is seems unwarranted to interpret conditions that result in low or even transient negative growth in terms of stress, as did, e.g. Bayne (1973).

The bivalve paradox

It may be a major factor in the many contradictory results and interpretations concerning bivalve water processing and feeding that bivalves are at the same time sensitive and tolerant towards their environment, depending upon the criteria used to assess sensitivity. If we use the pattern of activity of adductor muscles, mantle edges and rate of water processing as criteria the bivalves are extremely sensitive, reacting on the weakest mechanical stimulus and on chemical changes in the environment yet too subtle to be measured or identified. However, if we use sustained, apparently normal function and behaviour as well as survival as criteria, the bivalves are remarkably resistent.

An understanding of this apparent paradox may again be found at the level of the organism–environment entity. Suspension-feeding bivalves live in nutritionally highly dilute environments. In order to obtain food for maintenance and growth the animals must process large amounts of the ambient water, exposing the unprotected body surface to the environment. The great sensitivity towards external stimuli may therefore constitute a means of practically sessile organisms to reduce or avoid contact with an adverse environment.

The concurrent sensitivity and tolerance towards the environment is also reflected in the highly plastic growth and survival exhibited by bivalves, especially such species that inhabit biotopes extending into the tidal zone. In these, e.g., the mussel *Mytilus edulis* and the cockle *Cerastoderma edule* (Jones, 1979), reduction in valve gape or closure of the valves may constitute part of the normal activity in response to periods of depleted food or oxygen in the ambient water or to exposure at low tide. Members of a population may exhibit extreme differences in the degree to which they exploit their potential for growth, not as a result of physiological control of the rate of water processing, but directly as a result of the local environment of the individual bivalve.

The bivalve paradox includes one more facet. So far optimal environmental conditions have been identified with conditions compatible with the full exploitation of the potential for growth. However, if length of life is used as a measure of optimality the order is reversed, again exemplified in bivalve populations that extend into the tidal zone. Here the mussels and cockles that inhabit the marginal upper part of the zone tend to live longer than those from the lower part or below the zone (Seed, 1968, 1969; Jones, 1979). Growth rate and life expectancy thus seem interrelated and integrated with the environment.

[*90*]

CHAPTER XVI

Impact of bivalve filtration

It was argued above that suspension-feeding bivalves process the ambient water at rates that were evolutionarily adapted to the concentrations of phytoplankton that prevail during the productive seasons of the year. In order to exploit its potential for growth the individual bivalve should therefore be exposed to these concentrations. Most suspension-feeding bivalves are sessile with restricted means of actively acquiring fresh water, undepleted of food. Most suspension feeders eject the filtered water as a jet that pre-

Table 11. Bivalves: maximum population densities.

Species	Habitat	Dry mass of soft tissues, kg m^{-2}	Reference
Mytilus edulis	Intertidal	0.1-0.4	Dare, 1976
	Sublittoral	1.4	
Geukensia (Modiolus) demissa	Salt marsh	0.03-0.3	Kuenzler, 1961; Jordan & Valiela,1982
Cardium (Cerastoderma) edule	Intertidal	0.40	Dare, 1976
Ostrea edulis	Intertidal	0.20	Dare, 1976
Mya arenaria	Sublittoral	0.06	Dare, 1976

vents recirculation of the exhaled food-depleted water (see Jørgensen, 1966). However, such jet currents only affect the water circulation in the immediate vicinity of the organism. Sessile organisms therefore depend upon ambient water currents, and the densities that populations of suspension feeders may reach in a locality vary with the strength and constancy of the water currents that carry untaxed food supplies to the population. The highest densities are reached by bivalves (Table 11). High densities of suspension-feeding bivalves may substantially affect their environments. Such impact may materialize as biodeposition, control of phytoplankton growth and oxygen depletion, depending upon circumstances.

Biodeposition

In shallow waters with strong currents, e.g., due to pronounced tides, sedimented matter is resuspended, and the concentrations of particulate matter, seston, in the water may run as high as 100 mg l^{-1} or more, e.g., in the Wadden Sea, bordering the southern part of the North Sea (Gry, 1942; Havinga, 1954). In such biotopes suspension-feeding bivalves are exposed to much higher particle loads than can be ingested, and surplus matter is expelled as pseudofaeces. Mussels and oysters, which may inhabit highly turbid waters, begin to produce pseudofaeces at seston concentrations of a few mg l^{-1}. Moreover, seston in such habitats mostly consists of silt and detritus of no or little nutritional value, and most of the ingested matter is egested as true faeces. Both faeces and pseudofaeces sediment more rapidly than does the suspended matter from which they originate. Thus, the water-processing activity of suspension-feeding bivalves enhances the rate of deposition of the seston. The biodeposits also change the rheological properties of the sediments, which they stabilize (Sornin, 1983). However, biodeposits may also become resuspended at increased turbulence of the water, e.g., in connection with flooding and ebbing tidal currents.

The rate of turnover of biodeposits can be estimated from the rates at which pseudofaeces and faeces are produced and the actual rates of biodeposition. Obviously, the turnover rate will vary with the degree of turbulence that characterizes the habitat. The rate at which a population of suspension-feeding bivalves produces biodeposits is the difference between the rate at which the bivalves clear the water of seston and the digested and absorbed fraction of ingested matter. At high seston levels this fraction is insignificant. The contribution of the population to sedimentation therefore depends upon how large a fraction of the pseudofaeces and faeces remains permanently deposited. It is thus of interest to determine rates of net biodeposition by a population of suspension-feeding bivalves and to compare these rates with the maximum capacity for biodeposition, calculated as the product of rate of filtration and concentration of particulate matter that is efficiently retained by the filters.

The sedimentological and ecological importance of biodeposition is generally acknowledged, but few attempts have been made to quantify biodeposition in populations of suspension-feeding bivalves or other benthic suspension feeders. Verwey (1952) provided rough estimates of biodeposition

[92]

associated with beds of cockles *Cerastoderma edule* and mussels *Mytilus edulis* in the Dutch Wadden Sea. The estimates were based on known concentrations of seston in the water and filtration rates, which at that time were underestimated. Lund (1957) made similar estimates for oysters, *Crassostrea virginica*. More recently, rates of biodeposition have been directly measured in oysters kept in trays in running water, pumped from the outside. Haven & Morales-Alamo (1966) found that *C. virginica*, exposed to a mean seston concentration of about 9 mg l^{-1}, deposited from 4 to 9 g per g dry body mass per month in experiments performed during April, June-July and August with water pumped from the York River, Virginia, USA. Bernard (1974b) measured the annual biodeposition in the Pacific oyster, *Crassostrea gigas*. In July and September, values were 9-10 g per g dry body mass and month when the water, pumped from Departure Bay, British Columbia, Canada, contained seston at mean concentrations of 42 mg l^{-1} (July) and 21 mg l^{-1} (September).

The rates of biodeposition may be compared with the rates at which undisturbed oysters process the water and produce pseudofaeces and faeces. Pumping rates in *C. virginica* have been determined as a function of body mass by Riisgård (1988a) (Table 10, p. 86). From these rates and a mean concentration of 9 mg filterable seston per litre of sea water the rates at which oysters produce pseudofaeces + faeces amount to about 40-54 g per g dry body mass and month. The actually measured biodeposits thus constituted 10-16 % of the theoretical maximum. Assuming that the mass specific pumping rates in *C. gigas* is similar to those in *C. virginica*, calculations indicate that the measured rates of biodeposition amounted to 0.7 % of the theoretical maximum in July and 1.3 % in September (Bernard, 1974b).

The discrepancies between actually measured and maximally possible biodeposits have yet to be explained. Presumably, seston was assessed as particulate matter retained on a 0.45 μm pore-size filter, whereas the lower size limit for efficient retention of particles in the oyster gill filter is about 5 μm (Table 2, p. 31). But usually the greater part of seston is filterable by bivalves, so other factors must be considered, such as recirculation of water in the trays.

Measurements of biodeposition under controlled conditions in the laboratory can serve to assess the depositing capacities of populations of suspension-feeding bivalves. It seems, however, that optimal conditions for the production of biodeposits may not yet have been reached. Moreover, laboratory measurements of rates of biodeposition may be difficult to interpret

[*93*]

in sedimentological terms, applying to the natural beds, where, as mentioned, turnover rates of the biodeposits depends upon the turbulence which both varies with the tidal cycle and geographically. In the Dutch Wadden Sea, the greater part of material deposited by the mussel and cockle populations was resuspended immediately (Smaal *et al.*, 1986).

In the Baltic, Kautsky & Evans (1987) obtained more realistic data on the role of biodeposition by *Mytilus edulis* by recording seasonal deposition in sediment traps covered by mussels at natural densities. It was estimated that the mussel populations increased the total annual deposition of C, N and P by 10 %, and that the populations circulated and regenerated 12 and 22 %, respectively, of the annual N and P demands for pelagic primary production, thus playing an important role as a connecting link between the pelagic and benthic ecosystems in the area.

Doering & Oviatt (1986) determined biodeposition in outdoor mesocosm tanks (13 m^3) stocked with clams, *Mercenaria mercenaria*. Gross sedimentation was much below that expected by clams processing the water at their full capacities. The authors drew the unwarranted conclusion that filtration rates measured under optimal conditions in the laboratory do not apply in nature and therefore exaggerate the role of suspension-feeding bivalves in removal of particulate matter.

Effects on phytoplankton production

Dense populations of suspension-feeding bivalves may process the ambient water at such high rates that the populations of bivalves affect and even control phytoplankton production. Cloern (1982) provided evidence for such control in South San Francisco Bay. This shallow area receives large inputs of nutrients; however, despite eutrophication the standing biomass of phytoplankton remained low. The grazing by zooplankton accounted for only a small reduction in the net rate of phytoplankton growth. But calculations, based on the biomass and size distribution of benthic suspension-feeding bivalves and realistic rates of water filtration showed that the bivalve populations filtered a volume of water daily that exceeded the total volume of the shallow waters. It is thus suggested that bivalve grazing is the main factor in controlling phytoplankton biomass in South San Francisco Bay. In connection with Cloern's study, Officer *et al.* (1982) 'searched the literature for other examples in which the benthic filter-feeding population may exert a control, or be an important constituent, in the delineation of the phytoplankton population.' The authors found convincing evidence for such control in two other regions, the Pamlico estuary and Core and Bogue Sounds, both North Carolina, USA. The benthos in Pamlico estuary is dominated by large populations of the small bivalve *Rangia cuneata*, whereas in Core and Bogue Sounds the filter-feeding population is dominated by the clam *Mercenaria mercenaria* and the scallop *Aequipecten irradians*. Other examples have now been identified. In the intertidal zone of salt marshes along the east coast of the USA, the ribbed mussel *Geukensia demissa* may form dense populations with biomasses up to 0.1 kg m^{-2} or more (Table 11). Jordan & Valiela (1982) assessed the importance of the mussel in the nitrogen flow in a New England salt marsh, the Great Sippewissett Marsh, from determinations of filtration rates and rates of biodeposition. They calculated that during each tidal cycle in summer, the mussels filtered a volume of water in excess of the tidal volume of the marsh. The volume filtered is underestimated because filtration rates measured increased with body mass only according to an exponent of 0.39, whereas biodeposition, as measured in undisturbed mussels, increased with body mass according to the exponent 0.86, which must reflect the true exponent in the allometric relation between filtration rate and body mass. This was confirmed by Riisgård (1988) who obtained a value of 0.83 in undisturbed filtering mussels (Table 10, p. 86). Presumably, the low exponent found by Jordan & Valiela (1982) arises from the previously mentioned fact that the larger the mussels the more easily they are disturbed by the experimental procedure. It thus seems likely that in salt marshes where *Geukensia demissa* establish dense populations they significantly affect biomass and production of phytoplankton.

A further example of such impact was reported from Potomac River, Maryland, where Cohen *et al.* (1984) found that reduction in phytoplankton concentrations was inversely related to the density of the clam *Corbicula fluminea*. Determinations of filtration rates showed that the densest *Corbicula* populations would process a volume of water equivalent to the entire water column in 3-4 days.

Mussel beds

The impact of filter-feeding on the ambient water increases with increasing population density. Beds of mussels (*Mytilus edulis*) represent by far the highest population densities reached by any suspension-feeding organisms (Table 11). Densities of about 1 kg dry body mass per m² are typical of mussel beds from various types of habitat, both from the tidal zone (Dare, 1976; Fréchette *et al.* 1989; Wright *et al.*, 1982) and from sublittoral habitats (Dare, 1976; Jørgensen, 1980; Anders Randløv, personal communication).

The rates at which mussel beds process the surrounding water can be estimated from the size frequency distribution of mussels on the beds and the relation between size and clearance. Table 12 lists some estimates made from maximum densities of mussel beds from various intertidal and sublittoral localities. Rates of water processing amounting to about $10 \, \text{m}^3 \, \text{m}^{-2} \, \text{h}^{-1}$ seem to be typical. The impact of such rates may be assessed if we know the

Table 12. *Mytilus edulis*. Maximum rates of water processing by mussel beds.

Locality	Habitat	Clearance, $\text{m}^3 \, \text{m}^{-2} \, \text{h}^{-1}$	Reference
England	Intertidal	7	Dare, 1976
Canada	Intertidal	6	Fréchette *et al.*, 1989
England	Sublittoral	12	Dare, 1976
Denmark	Sublittoral	7	Jørgensen, 1980
–	–	8	Anders Randløv, personal communication

efficiency with which the mussels retain the various constituents, suspended or dissolved, in the ambient water. Besides phytoplankton, detritus and silt, these constituents include bacterioplankton and small organic molecules, particularly amino acids, as well as oxygen.

As mentioned, the lower size limit for efficient retention of suspended particles in the bivalve filters is some few μm in diameter (Table 2, p. 31). Bacterioplankton consists of mostly less than 1 μm cells. It is therefore not available to mussels such as *Mytilus edulis* (Wright *et al.*, 1982; Wildish & Kristmanson, 1984). There are reports on high efficiencies of retention of planktonic bacteria by some mussels, e.g., the ribbed mussel *Geukensia demissa* and the horse mussel *Modiolus modiolus*. Thus, Wright *et al.* (1982) found *G. demissa* to clear water of bacterioplankton with about 50%

efficiency, and they suggested that in salt marshes dense populations of *G. demissa* may exert significant grazing pressure on the bacteria. Wildish & Kristmanson (1984) examined depletion of seston from water passing an artificial mussel bed in a laboratory flume, and they found that *M. modiolus*, in contrast to *M. edulis*, significantly depleted the water of bacteria. However, the results seem inconclusive, because in both experiments the mussels were filtering at low rates only. In unrestrained animals, both of *G. demissa* and *M. modiolus*, the efficiency of particle retention was found to be similar to that in *M. edulis* (Table 2). It may thus be concluded that grazing of filter-feeding bivalves on the bacterioplankton is insignificant.

The inefficient retention of bacterioplankton is in contrast to the relatively efficient extraction of dissolved amino acids in the water passing the mantle cavity. *Mytilus edulis* thus extracted about 50 to 75 % or more of a number of different amino acids, present at concentrations of ≤ 1 μmol l^{-1} (Jørgensen, 1983b; Manahan *et al.*, 1983). However, the high extraction of amino acids from the water passing the mantle cavity was obtained in mussels that were starved of amino acids by being stored in amino acid depleted water. Such mussels, when placed in a restricted volume of water containing amino acids at μmolar concentrations, reduced the concentrations to non-detectable levels, whereas mussels that had previously been exposed to mmolar concentrations of amino acids exhibited net losses of amino acid (Jørgensen, 1983b).

The net uptake rate of amino acids in mussels in equilibrium with natural concentrations of amino acids may be lower than in mussels starved of amino acids. Thus, Siebers & Winkler (1984) pumped sea water from the Wadden Sea through tubes, densely filled with freshly collected *M. edulis*, and analysed ingoing and outgoing water for amino acids. Experiments were made in July and October, at total concentrations that ranged from about 0.7 to 2.4 μmol l^{-1}. The reduction in amino acid concentration was $43 \pm 12\,(SD)\%$ (n = 8). But flow through the tube was at a rate similar to the filtration rate of the mussels, implying substantial recirculation of the water, which may have increased extraction substantially. Gorham (1988) found freshly collected *M. edulis* to extract amino acids, present in the through current at μmolar concentrations, with efficiencies that ranged from about 20 % (serine and glutamic acid) to about 30 % (alanine) and 40 % (glycine).

As an example of the impact of water processing on the ambient water, consider a 50 m wide mussel bed, dominated by 5-7 cm long mussels which are capable of keeping a layer of water about 0.5 m deep circulated by means of the water currents they produce. If the mussels process the water at a rate of 8 m^3 m^{-2} h^{-1} a 1 m broad transsectional area of the bed will process 7 m^3 min^{-1}, or 28% of the accessible volume of 25 m^3 over the bed. From the rate of water processing and efficiencies of retention, the relations between pass time (t) and decrease in concentration of the various suspended or dissolved components of the passing water can be calculated from the clearance equation: $C_t = C_0 e^{-mt/M}$, where C_t and C_0 are downstream and upstream concentrations, M is the volume of water accessible to the mussels, and m the volume cleared per min.

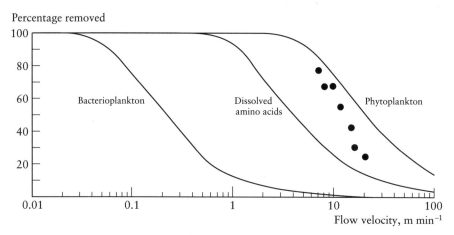

Figure 31. *Mytilus edulis*. Estimated relationship between flow velocity of water across a mussel bed and removal of various constituents from the water. The measured percentage removal of phytoplankton, ●, is calculated from Wright *et al.* (1982) (from Jørgensen, 1984).

The effects have been calculated as percentages of constituents removed from the passing water; the retention efficiencies used are 100% for phytoplankton, 20% for dissolved amino acids, and 1% for bacterioplankton. It may be seen from Figure 31 that this model mussel bed will practically completely deplete the water of phytoplankton at flow velocities of a few metres per min, velocities at which significant amounts of dissolved amino acids, but only negligible amounts of the bacterioplankton are removed. The bacterioplankton becomes heavily grazed only at the very low velocities of ≤ 0.1 m min^{-1}. At typical velocities of water passing an intertidal mussel bed, around 10-20 m min^{-1}, the model predicts that up to half the phytoplankton

[*98*]

is removed during the passage against some 20% of the dissolved amino acids, whereas the effect on the bacterioplankton is negligible. The predictions of the model are in reasonable agreement with Wright *et al.* (1982), whose data have been used to calculate the percentage of phytoplankton removed from the water passing a 46.5 m wide intertidal mussel bed. The percentages ranged from 77 to 24 at velocities ranging from 7 to 20 m min^{-1} (Figure 31). There was no measurable change in number of bacteria in the water passing the mussel bed.

It is thus indicated that within a restricted range of flow velocities over mussel beds the mussels may practically deplete the water of substrate for growth of the bacterioplankton without interfering directly with the bacteria. Presumably, such situations only apply for restricted periods to mussel beds exposed to the tidal cycles, or to sublittoral mussel beds that depend on water currents generated by the winds.

Spawning of mussels in a bed may be restricted to a short period of rising temperature in the spring, and in localities with low exchange of water masses the larvae may dominate the zooplankton until they metamorphose and settle. At such localities, the water-processing activity of the mussel larvae may greatly affect production and biomass of the nannoplankton. In the Isefjord, Denmark, a cohort of mussel larvae was found to process 0.4-0.5 l d^{-1} throughout its residence in the plankton, which lasted about one month. During this time the larvae might thus clear about 40-50% of the surrounding water daily of small food particles (Jørgensen, 1981c).

Oxygen depletion

Dense populations of bivalves, such as mussel beds, thus depends upon currents, tidal or produced by winds. In the absence of currents the bottom water above the beds is rapidly depleted of food and oxygen. Stagnation of the bottom water occurs as a seasonal phenomenon in many bays and fjords with more or less stable thermal stratification during summer when oxygen consumption by the benthos is maximal. Under such conditions oxygen concentrations in the bottom water decreases, particularly above mussel beds. The effects of stagnant bottom water during warm summers were studied in the Limfjord, Denmark (Jørgensen, 1980). The enhanced oxygen depletion above a mussel bed was demonstrated with an oxygen electrode mounted

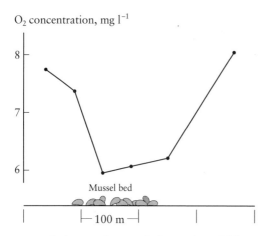

O$_2$ concentration, mg l^{-1}

Mussel bed

⊢ 100 m ⊣

Figure 32. Oxygen concentration in the bottom water, 3-4 cm above the sediment, on a mussel bed (*Mytilus edulis*) surrounded by mud flats (from Jørgensen, 1980).

on a sledge and towed through a 100 m wide area densely populated by mussels. Figure 32 shows that, although there was no general oxygen depletion of the bottom water in this area, the oxygen concentration dropped by 2 mg l^{-1} over the mussel bed. At another occasion the oxygen concentration was as low as 0.6 mg O$_2$ l^{-1}. *In situ* measurements showed that the rate of oxygen uptake of the mussel bed was more than ten times higher than of the surrounding bottom, namely 260 mmol m^{-2} d^{-1} against 22 mmol m^{-2} d^{-1}. The mussels accounted for the total consumption of oxygen of the bed. In food and oxygen depleted water the mussels with closed valves could survive the anoxia for 1-2 weeks. When they were dying, the valves opened and they soon started to decompose. This stimulated the growth of sulphur bacteria which oxidized H$_2$S released during the decomposition.

The periods of stagnant, oxygen depleted bottom water might last for a month or more. This caused mass mortality of the benthic fauna in local areas, besides the extinction of the mussel beds. Stagnation is usually broken up by western winds and the anoxic water is displaced by oxic water permitting recolonization of the mussel beds by settling veliger larvae.

CHAPTER XVII

Passive filter feeding

The establishment of dense populations of suspension feeders, including beds of mussels and other bivalves, thus depends upon external environmental currents, e.g. tidal or wind-generated, in order to avoid depletion of food particles in the boundary layer. However, external currents may not only deliver water replete of food particles for active processing in suspension feeders. The currents may also induce passive filter feeding, either as the only means of acquiring food or combined with active water processing.

The most clear-cut examples of passive filter feeding are to be found in some aquatic insect larvae that establish filtering nets across currents, e.g., *Trichoptera* larvae (Wallace & Malas, 1976a, b), or possess filtering devices in form of cephalic fans, such as Simuliidae larvae (Braimah, 1987a,b; Chance & Craig, 1986; Ross & Craig, 1980).

Passive filtration has also been ascribed an auxiliary role in typically active filter feeders, such as sponges (Vogel 1974, 1977, 1981), brachiopods (Eshleman & Wilkins, 1979; LaBarbera, 1977, 1984), sabellid polychaetes (Merz, 1984), scallops (Hartnoll, 1967) and the stalked ascidian *Styela montereyensis* (Young & Braithwaite, 1980).

The stalked ascidian seems to be the best documented example of the importance of passive filtration. The species occupies shallow water, with oscillating surge in which the animals orient themselves with the inhalant siphon constantly facing the current. Mechanical prevention of such orientation reduced fecal production by an average of about 60 %.

Vogel (1974) showed that external currents enhance the flow through a sponge, assessed from the velocity of the jet leaving the osculum, the sponge fingers acting as pitot tubes. The linear increase in the through current with velocity of the external current varied. In three examples (Vogel, 1977) the increase at an external current of 30 cm s^{-1} ranged from 22 to 85 %. Active water processing in sponges depends upon filtration of the water by the filament collar surrounding the flagellum of the choanocytes, the unit filter-pump of the flagellated chambers (Fjerdingstad, 1961). The passive flow

[101]

component induced by external currents may bypass this filter pump. It therefore remains to be ascertained to which extent the passive flow increases the rate and efficiency with which the sponge clear the through current of food and other particles.

Articulate brachiopods and scallops tend to orient themselves in relation to water currents, and this behaviour has been assumed to induce passive filtration (Eshleman & Wilkins, 1979; Hartnoll, 1967; LaBarbera 1977, 1981). At least in bivalves, however, a hydrostatic pressure imposed on the inhalant side of the gill pump does not significantly increase the filtration rate (Famme *et al.*, 1986). At the normal operating point of the pump of about 1 mm H_2O, the demibranches are inflated, exerting little frictional resistance to water flow. However, a slight positive pressure, of the order of ≥ 1 mm H_2O, may deflate the demibranchs, thus increasing resistance to flow and offsetting any effect of the pressure in terms of passive filtration. It remains to be seen whether similar conditions apply to brachiopods.

The importance of passive water transport through suspension feeders induced by external currents has been emphasized particularly by Vogel and his school. Passive components of the through current or behavioural orientation in relation to external currents are suggested to be adaptations, evolved in response to high costs of active water processing (LaBarbera, 1977, 1984; Vogel, 1974; Young & Braithwaite, 1980). However, as argued above, pp. 62 and 68, such interpretation seems ill-founded. In the giant scallop, Wildish *et al.* (1987) suggested that orientation in relation to external currents serves to secure active filtration in areas with strong currents. Presumably, the biological significance of orientation behaviour as well as passive water transport through suspension feeders occupying habitats with strong water currents needs further elucidation.

CHAPTER XVIII

Exploitation of filter feeding: shellfish culture

The rate of growth of filter-feeding bivalves, such as mussels, is genetically determined (Rodhouse *et al.*, 1986), but in dense populations growth may primarily depend upon the supply of food, implying access to untaxed food sources. Thus, bivalves that occupy the upstream part of a bed will grow faster than those downstream, which feed on waters that are more or less depleted of food. But the microhabitat of the individual bivalve may be equally important. In gregarious species, such as mussels, individuals on the outside of a cluster exposed to the free water masses receive more food and grow faster than those deeper in the cluster. At the extreme, individuals deep in a cluster may end up feeding on water that is depleted of food to below maintenance levels. The fastest growing individuals in a mussel bed are those most likely to survive and to produce most offspring.

In natural beds of mussels, oysters and other gregarious suspension-feeding bivalves the greater part of the population may not fully exploit its potential for growth (Boromthanarat & Deslous-Paoli, 1988; Fréchette & Bourget, 1985a, Loo & Rosenberg, 1989; Wildish, 1977; Wildish & Kristmanson, 1985). This fact is the basis for the culture of mussels. The principle of such culture is to improve the access to undepleted food sources. This can be done by establishing settling facilities in the water column in form of ropes or strings, hanging down from anchored rafts that float on the surface. Substrates for settling of veliger larvae are placed in localities, within the reach of veligers from natural mussel beds, with high production of phytoplankton and appropriate and stable water currents to maintain the supply of food. As the water flows through such suspended mussel cultures the phytoplankton is grazed. The density of ropes or strings and depth of the culture belt compatible with high and uniform growth of mussels that settle within the belt therefore varies with the productivity of the locality and strength and constancy of the water currents.

Mussel culture is an old tradition in Spain, but is rapidly spreading to northern Europe and North America (Table 13). These cultures have revealed high unused potentials for production in natural mussel beds. The

[103]

Table 13. *Mytilus edulis*. Time from settlement to a shell length of 5-6 cm in cultured mussels (from Loo & Rosenberg, 1983).

Locality	Time, months
Norway and Sweden	14-16
Scotland and Wales	16-18
Netherlands	20*
France	12-18
Spain	8-10
Rhode Island and Massachusetts, USA	12-13
Maine, USA	12-22
New Brunswick, Canada	24-28
Newfoundland, Canada	34-35

* Probably bottom cultured mussels

growth rates of mussels in cultures are remarkably similar in the various geographical areas, primarily determined by the level of phytoplankton production and duration of the annual productive period. The particularly high rates obtaining in mussel culture in Spain may result from thinning of the young mussels, a process that reduces competition for food among the remaining mussels. Table 13 shows that cultured young mussels typically grow at a mean annual rate of ≥ 0.1 mm per day or ≥ 3 mm a month. This corresponds to growth rates obtained under optimal conditions in net bags during the seasons of high phytoplankton production (Table 8, p. 80). The cultures therefore efficiently exploit the inherent potential for growth of the mussels.

CHAPTER XIX

The 'Mussel Watch'

The last few decades have witnessed an increasing awareness of the threats to the marine environment resulting from the introduction of human waste. During an early period, radioactive waste from surface testing of nuclear weapons was the great concern, but more recently focus has moved to industrial, agricultural and household wastes as the dominant sources of pollution of the marine environment.

[*104*]

Three main categories of wastes may be distinguished, only two of which are pollutants in a strict sense of the word. These two constitute metals, particularly heavy metals, and organochlorines. The third group encompasses organic waste and fertilizers, that is, compounds and substances that already are constituents of any ecosystem as basic components in the primary production. Addition of these components may therefore result in a higher rate of primary production, particularly of phytoplankton, and thus give rise to eutrophication of the environment that may drastically change the balance of the ecosystem. The possible role of filter-feeding bivalves in such a balance was mentioned above, p. 94.

Heavy metals are waste products in many metallurgic and other industrial processes, the organochlorines and similar compounds are derived from the chemical industry, ranging from the production of synthetic materials to pesticides and their use in pest control. The most important heavy metals are copper, zinc, lead, mercury and cadmium, and important organochlorines are the pesticides DDT, aldrin, heptachlor, lindane and the non-pesticide biphenyls (PCBs) (Phillips, 1980).

The introduction of pollutants into the environment initiated programmes for the systematic monitoring of the pollutants, including those entering the ocean with rivers or waste pipes and from the air, mainly with the precipitation. Pollutants mostly occur in trace amounts, and their quantification depended upon the development of techniques sufficiently sensitive and accurate for their determination. Many analyses require highly sophisticated and expensive instrumentation, including gas chromatography, high pressure liquid chromatography, neutron activation analysis and atomic absorption spectrophotometry (Goldberg, 1976).

Costly and often laborious analysis is one disadvantage of the direct assessment of pollutant levels in the sea and other aquatic habitats. Another disadvantage is the often extreme variation in pollutant levels in natural waters with time. Such variation may be seasonal, or depend upon tides and currents, or upon intermittent flow of industrial effluents. Moreover, difficulties may arise in the interpretation of the analytical data in terms of biological availability of the pollutant present in the water. The biological availability depends upon the state in which the pollutant is present in the water, whether in solution or sequestered in complexes which may be inaccessible to the organisms. Both heavy metals and organochlorines may form chelates and complexes, varying with the salinity of the water, which make the pollutants unavailable to organisms. Monitoring programmes for marine pollution therefore turned to the analyses of the organisms exposed to the pollutants, and an important question to answer was which organisms to choose as monitoring organisms. Goldberg (1975) was very successful in advocating mussels (*Mytilus edulis* and related species) in a global monitoring programme, known as the 'Mussel Watch' programme.

Mussels probably fulfill what should be required from a candidate in global monitoring to a higher degree than any other organism. The most important requirements include the following. The organism should (1) accumulate the pollutant without being killed by the levels encountered in the environment, (2) be sedentary in order to be representative of the study area, (3) be abundant throughout the study area, (4) be of reasonable size, giving adequate tissue for analysis, (5) tolerate brackish water and (6) show a simple relation between pollutant content and pollutant concentration in the surrounding water (Bryan *et al.*, 1985; Phillips, 1980).

Of these requirements the last-mentioned is probably the most difficult to fulfill for any monitoring organism, including mussels. The relationship between mean pollutant concentration in the water and content in the organism may vary from simple to complex. In the case of hydrocarbons the relation is simple. Mussels take up hydrocarbons by simple diffusion and they do not possess specific means for dealing with the hydrocarbons, e.g., in the excretory organs. Mussels can therefore theoretically serve as simple integrators in the monitoring of oil pollution. Heavy metals on the other hand may both be taken up and excreted, or bound and detoxified by specific low molecular proteins, metallothioneins, as well as other proteins, or stored in granules or deposited in shells, etc. (George *et al.*, 1979; Köhler & Riisgård, 1982; Phillips, 1980). The content of a heavy metal in the organism at any time is therefore determined by complex kinetics. In order to interpret data on pollutant content in an organism the kinetics should be known, as well as how the kinetic parameters may vary with both external factors, such as temperature and salinity, and internal factors, such as age, size, sex, maturity and nutritional condition.

It was realized early on that the monitoring mussels should also be investigated for possible physiological effects of pollutants, particularly effects on growth, reproduction and storage of glycogen, that is, all aspects of the production term in the matter and energy balance of the organism (Bayne, 1976).

[*106*]

In order to assess the effects of pollutants on growth in mussels, the experimental set up must be compatible with the full exploitation of the growth potential in control mussels. It is thus a condition that any decline in the rate of water processing should be an effect of the pollutant. The same condition applies to kinetic studies. However, most investigations of pollutant kinetics as well as of physiological effects have been carried out on unfed mussels, which, as mentioned, process water below the capacity of the pump and thus below the uptake capacity of the pollutant (Janssen & Scholz, 1979; Köhler & Riisgård, 1982; Riisgård *et al.*, 1987).

A pollutant may affect water processing by reducing gaping of the valves and/or by acting directly on the ciliary pump. Davenport & Manley (1978) showed that *Mytilus edulis* responded with valve closure when gradually rising concentrations of copper (as $CuSO_4$) reached a concentration of only 0.021 ppm. At further rising concentrations the mussels showed 'testing' behaviour until at 0.2 ppm or more the valves remained closed, isolating the animal from the environment. In mussels that had been exposed to 0.02 ppm total copper in sea water for 10 days the initial reduction in valve gape occurred at a significantly higher copper concentration (0.16 ppm). The behaviour of mussels from unpolluted areas is thus highly sensitive to the addition of copper to the environment.

In order to investigate the effect of copper directly on the ciliary pump, Howell *et al.* (1984) cut the adductor muscle, thus preventing closure of the valves. Ciliary activity was assessed from the rate at which the operated mussels cleaned solutions of the dye methyl red. They found that a copper concentration of about 0.09 ppm reduced clearance by 50%. This effect of copper was abolished in mussels that had been treated with reserpine. The authors suggested that the mussels responded to the metal in the ambient water by a reduced rate of ciliary activity, mediated via the branchial nerve. However, severing the adductor muscle only prevents the closure of the valves and does not affect the closure response. As mentioned, this behavioural response is a complex of integrated muscular activities, including contraction of the adductor muscle, retraction of the mantle edges and siphon, as well as reduction of the length of the gill axes. The last effect reduces the power and capacity of the pump without necessarily affecting the ciliary activity. The interpretation in terms of a nerve-mediated effect of copper on the water-transporting cilia therefore seems unwarranted. The finding that treatment with reserpine abolished the effect of copper on the methyl-red clearance rather suggests that reserpine inhibited the closure response.

The behavioural response of isolating the organism from an adverse environment may be more sensitive to pollutants, such as heavy metals, than the physiological mechanisms involved in feeding and metabolism. Thus, in long-term experiments, body loads in mussels up to 150 ppm of cadmium did not affect either clearance, ingestion, assimilation, respiration or growth. Net growth efficiencies amounted to 55-59%, indicating near optimal experimental conditions. The cadmium load of 150 ppm was reached at a concentration of 100 ppb in the ambient water, which is many orders of magnitude higher than in unpolluted sea water (Poulsen *et al.*, 1982). *Mytilus edulis* may therefore be relatively tolerant to heavy metals, adding to its qualifications as a monitoring organism.

CHAPTER XX

Summary (Recapitulation)

The bivalve filter pump consists of pump units arranged in parallel. The unit is an interfilament canal lined by opposing bands of lateral cilia, which are situated close to the entrance to the canal. The pump is constructed to produce maximum pressure and flow when the valves are fully open and mantle edges and siphon(s) are extended, reflecting the relaxed, unrestrained condition of the organism. Reduced gaping of the valves and retraction of mantle edges and siphon(s) are coupled with reduced interfilament distance, which results in declining pump pressure and flow.

Filtration of the water passing through the interfilament canals implies transfer of suspended particles from the through currents at the entrance to the interfilament canals to surface currents along the frontal surface of the filaments. These ciliary currents continue in currents along the dorsal and/or ventral margin of the demibranchs, carrying particles in suspension towards the mouth and down the oesophagus. Only particles in suspension are normally being ingested. Particles that become entangled in mucus are transferred along rejection tracts to the mouth palps, converted into pseudofaeces and ejected. Mucus is secreted when the concentration of suspended matter in the ambient water exceeds the capacity for ingestion of matter retained by the filter.

Secreted mucus from isolated goblet cells on the gill filaments coalesce to form thin threads that tend to traverse the gill filaments. The threads move relatively slowly towards the ventral margins of the demibranchs and fast-moving particles suspended in the surface currents of the filaments may become caught in the mucus when they pass a thread. The chance of being caught, and thus of being ejected as pseudofaeces, presumably depends upon size, shape and other physical characteristics of the particles. Such properties of the particles may therefore constitute the basis for a selection mechanism that more or less efficiently secures the differential ingestion of food particles, such as algal cells, in the presence of excessive amounts of silt suspended in the water.

The gill filter does not act as a mechanical sieve, but fluid mechanical forces, arising in the complex pattern of laminar currents at the entrance to the interfilament canals, are presumably responsible for the transfer of particles across streamlines from the through currents to the surface currents. The fluid mechanics of this particle transfer, and thus capture, remains to be analysed.

Water pumping and filtration efficiency are basically autonomous processes, reflecting physical properties of the filter pump, and they are not subject to physiological regulation at the organismic level, e.g., according to nutritional needs. Feeding in filter-feeding bivalves is thus a highly automatized process, retention of particulate matter being determined by the capacity of the pump and the concentration of food in the ambient water.

The basic behavioural repertoire of filter-feeding bivalves spans from closed to fully open valves accompanied by extended mantle edges and siphon(s). The behaviour reflects the environmental conditions. In clean water that contains suspended food (phytoplankton) and silt in concentrations typical of the productive season of the habitat, filter-feeding bivalves respond by adopting the latter behaviour, in which state only, the filter pump processes the ambient water at its full capacity. Conditions that are compatible with the fully open state may therefore be characterized as optimal. The bivalves may respond to the environment by reduction of the valve gape and retraction of mantle edges and siphon and the environment may be termed

[*109*]

adverse. Adverse environmental factors include low concentrations of suspended particles, lack of oxygen and foul water.

The capacity for water processing is evolutionarily adapted to the concentrations of suspended food, primarily phytoplankton, that prevail in the biotope during the productive seasons of the year. During such periods the capacity for water processing enables the bivalve more or less fully to exploit its potential for growth, reproduction and/or deposition of glycogen, that is, the production potential.

Under adverse conditions, when water processing is reduced, growth declines and may become negative. At moderately reduced rates of water processing, the organism may remain in positive energy balance. In order to estimate effects on the energy balance, water processing should be assessed in terms of exploitation of the pump capacity. Such assessment can serve as a measure of the degree to which experimental conditions deviate from the optimal. Capacities for water processing and growth potentials are therefore fundamental parameters to ascertain.

Widely accepted views are incompatible with the present analysis of the function of the gill pump and of the behaviour of filter-feeding bivalves. According to these views water processing is physiologically regulated to secure a more or less constant ingestion rate at varying concentrations of suspended food particles. Moreover, it has been assumed that feeding is endogenously controlled according to seasonally induced rhythms. Theories implying such physiological control of feeding are interpretations of results obtained in experiments where particle clearances were observed to vary with particle concentration as well as with season. Typically, however, the clearances are low compared with the capacity of the filter pump and the experimental conditions have been incompatible with full exploitation of the growth potential. Results obtained under such conditions may be interpreted in terms of behaviour reflecting degrees of deviation from optimal conditions in nature.

Filter-feeding bivalves indiscriminately clear the water of suspended particles above threshold sizes for retention in the filters. This includes practically all components of the phytoplankton and the major proportion of inorganic particles and organic detritus. The great capacity of the pump implies a corresponding potential for depletion of the ambient water of suspended particulate matter. In areas with shallow water and currents that permit filter-feeding bivalves to establish dense populations, the filtering activity of these populations may materially affect the habitat, e.g., by determining rate of sedimentation and physical properties of the sediment, as well as by controlling the rate of phytoplankton production.

In gregarious filter-feeding bivalves, such as mussels, the dense populations may aggregate in beds in which the access to food vary greatly among individuals. Patchiness in availability of food results in greatly varying exploitation of potentials for growth among the members of the population. The production reserves in such localities may be utilized in culture of the population, based on the establishment of settling facilities in the form of strings or ropes anchored to floats and suspended in the water column.

Mussel beds may reach densities that result in the beds consuming oxygen at rates that are an order of magnitude higher per unit area than the rates at which the neighbouring sediments consume oxygen. In such localities seasonally occurring periods with stagnant water may lead to oxygen depletion over the beds. At lasting stagnation sulfide may enter the water and cause the death of the mussels and other organisms within the area. The frequency of such incidences may increase with eutrophication of the locality.

Besides particulate matter and oxygen, filter-feeding bivalves may efficiently retain other constituents present in the ambient water, including pollutants such as heavy metals and organochlorines. These constituents typically accumulate in the shells and soft parts of the body. Such bioaccumulation is the basis for the use of filter-feeding bivalves in pollution monitoring, exemplified in the global 'Mussel Watch' programmes.

References

AIELLO, E. (1960). Factors affecting ciliary activity on the gill of the mussel *Mytilus edulis*. *Physiological Zoology* 33, 120-135.

AIELLO, E. (1970). Nervous and chemical stimulation of gill cilia in bivalve molluscs. *Physiological Zoology* 43, 60-70.

AIELLO, E. & SLEIGH, M.A. (1972). The metachronal wave of lateral cilia of *Mytilus edulis*. *The Journal of Cell Biology* 54, 493-506.

ALDER, J. & HANCOCK, A. (1851). On the branchial currents in *Pholas* and *Mya*. *Magazine of Natural History* 8, 2nd series, 370-378.

ALI, R.M. (1970). The influence of suspension density and temperature on the filtration rate of *Hiatella arctica*. *Marine Biology* 6, 291-302.

ALLEN, J.A. (1958). On the basic form and adaptations to habitat in the Lucinacea (Eulamellibranchia). *Philosophical Transactions of the Royal Society* Series B 241, 421-484.

ALLEN, J.A. (1968). The functional morphology of *Crassinella mactracea* (Linsley) (Bivalvia: Astartacea). *Proceedings of the Malacological Society, London* 38, 27-40.

ALLEN, T.F.H. & STARR, T.B. (1982). Hierarchy: Perspectives for Ecological Complexity. University of Chicago Press, Chicago.

AMOUROUX, J.-M., D'ALLONES, M.R. & ROUAULT, C. (1975). Sur la mesure directe du débit de filtration chez les mollusques lamellibranches. *Vie et Milieu* 25, 339-346.

ANDERSEN, V., NIVAL, P. & HARRIS, R.P. (1987). Modelling of a planktonic ecosystem in an enclosed water column. *Journal of the Marine Biological Association of the United Kingdom* 67, 407-430.

ANSELL, A.D. (1961). The functional morphology of the British species of Veneracea (Eulamellibranchia). *Journal of the Marine Biological Association of the United Kingdom* 41, 489-515.

ANSELL, A.D. (1981). Functional morphology and feeding of *Donax serra* Röding and *Donax sordidus* Hanley (Bivalvia: Donacidae). *Journal of Molluscan Studies* 47, 59-72.

ATKINS, D. (1936). On the ciliary mechanisms and interrelationships of lamellibranchs. Part I. Some new observations on sorting mechanisms in certain lamellibranchs. *Quarterly Journal of the Microscopical Society* 79, 181-308.

ATKINS, D. (1937a). On the ciliary mechanisms and interrelationships of lamellibranchs. Part II. Sorting devices on the gills. *Quarterly Journal of the Microscopical Society* 79, 339-373.

ATKINS, D. (1937b). On the ciliary mechanisms and interrelationships of lamellibranchs. Part III. Types of lamellibranch gills and their food currents. *Quarterly Journal of the Microscopical Society* 79, 375-421.

ATKINS, D. (1938). On the ciliary mechanisms and interrelationships of lamellibranchs. Part VII. Latero-frontal cilia of the gill filaments and their phylogenetic value. *Quarterly Journal of the Microscopical Society* 80, 345-436.

[*113*]

AYALA, F.J. & DOBZHANSKY, T. (eds.) (1974). Studies in the Philosophy of Biology. University of California Press, Berkeley.

BAIRD, R.H. (1966). Factors affecting growth and condition of mussels (*Mytilus edulis* L.). *Ministry of Agriculture, Fisheries and Food, Fishery Investigations* Series II, Volume XXV, Number 2, 1-33.

BAYNE, B.L. (1973). Physiological changes in *Mytilus edulis* L. induced by temperature and nutritive stress. *Journal of the Marine Biological Association of the United Kingdom* 53, 39-58.

BAYNE, B.L. (1976). Watch on mussels. *Marine Pollution Bulletin* 7, 217-218.

BAYNE, B.L. (1987). Genetic aspects of physiological adaptation in bivalve molluscs. *In* Evolutionary Physiological Ecology (ed. P. Calow), pp 169-189. Cambridge University Press, Cambridge.

BAYNE, B.L. & NEWELL, R.C. (1983). Physiological energetics of marine molluscs. *In* The Mollusca (ed. K.M. Wilbur), Vol. 4, Part 1, pp. 407-515, Academic Press, New York.

BAYNE, B.L. & SCULLARD, C. (1977). An apparent specific dynamic action in *Mytilus edulis* L. *Journal of the Marine Biological Association of the United Kingdom* 57, 371-378.

BAYNE, B.L. & WIDDOWS, J. (1978). The physiological ecology of two populations of *Mytilus edulis* L. *Oecologia* 37, 137-162.

BAYNE, B.L., HAWKINS, A.J.S. & NAVARRO, E. (1987). Feeding and digestion by the mussel *Mytilus edulis* L. (Bivalvia: Mollusca) in mixtures of silt and algal cells at low concentrations. *Journal of Experimental Marine Biology and Ecology* 111, 1-22.

BAYNE, B.L., HAWKINS, A.J.S. & NAVARRO, E. (1988). Feeding and digestion in suspension-feeding bivalve molluscs: The relevance of physiological compensations. *American Zoologist* 28, 147-159.

BAYNE, B.L., THOMPSON, R.J. & WIDDOWS. J. (1976). Physiology: I. *In* Marine Mussels: Their Ecology and Physiology (ed. B.L. Bayne), pp 121-206. Cambridge University Press, Cambridge.

BAYNE, B.L., WIDDOWS, J. & NEWELL, R.I.E. (1977). Physiological measurements on estuarine bivalve molluscs in the field. *In* Biology of Benthic Organisms (eds. B.F. Keegan, P. O'Céidigh & P.J.S. Boaden), pp. 57-68. Pergamon Press, Oxford.

BAYNE, B.L., BAYNE, C.J., CAREFOOT, T.C. & THOMPSON, R.J. (1976). The physiological ecology of *Mytilus californianus* Conrad. 1. Metabolism and energy balance. *Oecologia* 22, 211-228.

BAYNE, B.L., HAWKINS, A.J.S., NAVARRO, E. & IGLESIAS, I.P. (1989). Effects of seston concentration on feeding, digestion and growth in the mussel *Mytilus edulis*. *Marine Ecology Progress Series* 55, 47-54.

BERNARD, F.R. (1974a). Particle sorting and labial palp function in the Pacific oyster *Crassostrea gigas* (Thunberg, 1795). *Biological Bulletin of the Marine Biological Laboratory, Woods Hole* 146, 1-10.

BERNARD, F.R. (1974b). Annual biodeposition and gross energy budget of mature pacific oysters, *Crassostrea gigas*. *Journal of the Fishery Research Board of Canada* 31, 185-190.

BERNARD, F.R. (1983). Physiology and the mariculture of some north-eastern Pacific bivalve molluscs. *Canadian Fisheries and Aquatic Sciences, Special Publications* 63, 1-24.

REFERENCES

BLAKE, J. (1973). A note on mucus shear rates. *Respiration Physiology* 17, 394-399.

BLAKE, J.R. & SLEIGH, M.A. (1974). Mechanics of ciliary locomotion. *Biological Reviews* 49, 85-125.

BLAKE, J.R. & SLEIGH, M.A. (1975). Hydromechanical aspects of ciliary propulsion. *In* Swimming and Flying in Nature (eds. T.Y. Wu, C.J. Brokaw & C. Brennen). Vol. 1, pp. 185-209. Plenum Press, New York.

BØHLE, B. (1970). Forsøk med dyrking av blåskjell (*Mytilus edulis* L.) ved overføring av yngel til nettingstrømper. *Fiskets Gang* 1970, 267-271.

BONNET, R. (1877). Der Bau und die Circulationsverhältnisse der Acephalenkieme. *Morphologisches Jahrbuch* 3, 283-327.

BOOTH, C.E. & MANGUM, C.P. (1979). Oxygen uptake and transport in the lamellibranch mollusc *Modiolus demissus*. *Physiological Zoology* 51, 17-32.

BORCHARDT, T. (1985). Relationships between carbon and cadmium uptake in *Mytilus edulis*. *Marine Biology* 85, 233-244.

BOROMTHANARAT, S. & DESLOUS-PAOLI, J.M. (1988). Production of *Mytilus edulis* L. reared on bouchots in the Bay of Marennes-Oleron: Comparison between two methods of culture. *Aquaculture* 72, 255-263.

BRAIMAH, S.A. (1987a). Mechanisms of filter feeding in immature *Simulium bivittatum* Malloch (Diptera: Simuliidae) and *Isonychia campestris* McDunnough (Ephemeoptera: Oligoneuriidae) *Canadian Journal of Zoology* 65, 504-513.

BRAIMAH, S.A. (1987b). Pattern of flow around filter-feeding structures of immature *Simulium bivittatum* Malloch (Diptera: Simuliidae) and *Isonychia campestris* McDunnough (Ephemeoptera: Oligoneuriidae). *Canadian Journal of Zoology* 65, 514-521.

BRENNEN, C. & WINET, H. (1977). Fluid mechanics of propulsion by cilia and flagella. *Annual Review of Fluid Mechanics* 9: 339-398.

BRICELJ, V.M. & MALOUF, R.E. (1984). Influence of algal and suspended sediment concentrations on the feeding physiology of the hard clam *Mercenaria mercenaria*. *Marine Biology* 84, 155-165.

BRICELJ, V.M., MALOUF, R.E. & QUILLFELDT, C. DE (1984). Growth of juvenile *Mercenaria mercenaria* and the effect of resuspended bottom sediments. *Marine Biology* 84, 167-173.

BROKAW, C.J. & SIMONICK, T.F. (1977). Mechanochemical coupling in flagella. *Journal of Cell Science* 23, 227-241.

BRONN's (1862) Classen und Ordnungen des Thierreichs. Bd III, Abth. I. Kopflose Weichthiere (Malacozoa Acephala). Leipzig.

BROWN, S.C. (1977). Biomechanics of water-pumping by *Chaetopterus variopedatus* Renier: Kinetics and hydrodynamics. *Biological Bulletin of the Marine Biological Laboratory, Woods Hole* 153, 121-132.

BRYAN, G.W., LANGSTON, W.J., HUMMERSTONE, L.G. & BURT, G.R. (1985). A Guide to the Assessment of Heavy-Metal Contamination in Estuaries Using Biological Indicators. *Marine Biological Association of the United Kingdom*. Occasional Publication Number 4.

BULLIVANT, J.S. (1968). A revised classification of suspension feeders. *Tuatara* 16, 151-160.

[*115*]

BULLOCK, T.H. (1955). Compensation for temperature in the metabolism and activity of poikilotherms. *Biological Reviews* 30, 311-342.

BUSS, L.W. & JACKSON, J.B.C. (1981). Planktonic food availability and suspension-feeder abundance: evidence of *in situ* depletion. *Journal of Experimental Marine Biology and Ecology* 49, 151-161.

BUXTON, C.D., NEWELL, R.C. & FIELD, J.G. (1981). Response-surface analysis of the combined effects of exposure and acclimation temperatures on filtration, oxygen consumption and scope for growth in the oyster *Ostrea edulis*. *Marine Ecology Progress Series* 6, 73-82.

CATAPANE, E.J., STEFANO, G.B. & AIELLO, E. (1978). Pharmacological study of the reciprocal dual innervation of the lateral ciliated gill epithelium by the CNS of *Mytilus edulis* (Bivalvia). *Journal of Experimental Biology* 74, 101-113.

CATAPANE, E.J., STEFANO, G.B. & AIELLO, E. (1979). Neurophysiological correlates of the dopaminergic cilio-inhibitory mechanism of *Mytilus edulis*. *Journal of Experimental Biology* 83, 315-323.

CATAPANE, E.J., THOMAS, J., STEFANO, G., PAUL, D. (1981). Effects of temperature and temperature acclimation on serotonin-induced cilio-excitation of the gill of *Mytilus edulis*. *Journal of Thermal Biology* 6, 61-64.

CHANCE, M.M. & CRAIG, D.A. (1986). Hydrodynamics and behaviour of Simuliidae larvae (Diptera). *Canadian Journal of Zoology* 64, 1295-1309.

CHAPMAN, G. (1968). The hydraulic system of *Urechis caupo* Fisher & McGinitie. *Journal of Experimental Biology* 49, 657-667.

CHEUNG, A.T.W. & WINET, H. (1975). Flow velocity profile over a ciliated surface. *In* Swimming and Flying in Nature (eds. T.Y. Wu, C.J. Brokaw & C. Brennen), Vol. 2, pp. 223-234. Plenum Press, New York.

CHIPMAN, W.A. (1959). The use of radioisotopes in studies of the foods and feeding activities of marine animals. *Pubblicazioni della Stazione Zoologica di Napoli* 31, Suppl., 154-175.

CHIPMAN, W.A. & HOPKINS, J.G. (1954). Water filtration by the bay scallop, *Pecten irradians*, as observed with the use of radioactive plankton. *Biological Bulletin of the Marine Biological Laboratory, Woods Hole* 107, 90-91.

CHURCHILL, E.P. & LEWIS, S.I. (1924). Food and feeding in freshwater mussels. *Bulletin of the United States Bureau for Fishery* 39, 439-471.

CLAUSEN, C. (1958). On the anatomy and histology of the eulamellibranch *Kelliella miliaris* (Philippi) with observations on the ciliary mechanisms in the mantle cavity. *Nytt Magasin for Zoologi* 6, 144-175.

CLEMMESEN, B. & JØRGENSEN, C.B. (1987). Energetic costs and efficiencies of ciliary filter feeding. *Marine Biology* 94, 445-449.

CLOERN, J.E. (1982). Does the benthos control phytoplankton biomass in South San Francisco Bay? *Marine Ecology Progress Series* 9, 191-202.

COHEN, R.R.H., DRESLER, P.V., PHILLIPS, E.J.P. & CORY, R.L. (1984). The effect of the Asiatic clam, *Corbicula fluminea*, on phytoplankton of the Potomac River, Maryland. *Limnology and Oceanography* 26, 170-180.

REFERENCES

COLLIER, A. (1959). Some observations on the respiration of the American oyster *Crassostrea virginica* (Gmelin). *Institute of Marine Science* 6, 92-108.

COLLIER, A. & RAY, S.M. (1948). An automatic proportioning apparatus for experimental study of the effect of chemical solutions on aquatic animals. *Science* 107, 576.

CONOVER, R.J. (1966). Assimilation of organic matter by zooplankton. *Limnology and Oceanography* 11, 338-345.

CONRAD, M. (1976). Biological adaptability: the statistical state model. *Bio Science* 26, 319-324.

CONRAD, M. (1983). Adaptability. The Significance of Variability from Molecule to Ecosystem. Plenum Press, New York.

CORNER, E.D.S. (1961). On the nutrition and metabolism of zooplankton. I. Preliminary observations on the feeding of the marine copepod *Calanus helgolandicus* (Claus). *Journal of the Marine Biological Association of the United Kingdom* 41, 5-16.

COUGHLAN, J. (1969). The estimation of filtering rate from the clearance of suspensions. *Marine Biology* 2, 356-358.

COUGHLAN, J. & ANSELL, A.D. (1964). A direct method for determining the pumping rate of siphonate bivalves. *Journal du Conseil International pour l'Exploration de la Mer* 29, 205-213.

COULTHARD, H.S. (1929). Growth of the sea mussel. *Contribution to Canadian Biology and Fisheries*, New Series 4, 121-136.

COX, R.G. & HSU, S.K. (1977). The lateral migration of solid particles in laminar flow near a plane. *International Journal for Multiphase Flow* 3, 201-222.

CRISP, D.J. (1964). An assessment of plankton grazing by barnacles. *In* Grazing in Terrestrial and Marine Environments (ed. D.J. Crisp), pp 251-264. Blackwell, Oxford.

DAGG, M.J. & TURNER, J.T. (1982). The impact of copepod grazing on the phytoplankton of Georges Bank and the New York Bight. *Canadian Journal of Fishery and Aquatic Sciences* 39, 979-990.

DAME, R.F. & DANKERS, N. (1988). Uptake and release of materials by a Wadden Sea mussel bed. *Journal of Experimental Marine Biology and Ecology* 118, 207-216.

DARE, P.J. (1976). Settlement, growth, and production of the mussel, *Mytilus edulis* L., in Morecambe Bay, England. *Fishery Investigations Series* II, 28, No. 1, pp. 1-25.

DAVENPORT, J. & MANLEY, A. (1978). The detection of heightened sea-water copper concentrations by the mussel *Mytilus edulis*. *Journal of the Marine Biological Association of the United Kingdom* 58, 843-850.

DAVENPORT, J. & WOOLMINGTON, A.D. (1982). A new method of monitoring ventilatory activity in mussels and its use in a study of ventilatory patterns of *Mytilus edulis* L. *Journal of Experimental Marine Biology and Ecology* 62, 55-67.

DAVIDS, C. (1964). The influence of suspensions of microorganisms of different concentrations on the pumping rate and retention of food by the mussel (*Mytilus edulis* L.). *Netherlands Journal of Sea Research* 2, 233-249.

DENNY, M.W. & GOSLINE, J.M. (1980). The physical properties of the pedal mucus of the terrestrial slug, *Ariolimax columbinus*. *Journal of Experimental Biology* 88, 375-393.

DOBZHANSKY, T. (1941). Genetics and the Origin of Species. (2. ed.) Columbia University Press, New York.

[*117*]

DOERING, P.H. & OVIATT, C.A. (1986). Application of filtration rate models to field populations of bivalves: an assessment using experimental mesocosms. *Marine Ecology Progress Series* 31, 265-275.

DRAL, A.D.G. (1967). The movement of the latero-frontal cilia and the mechanism of particle retention in the mussel (*Mytilus edulis* L.). *Netherlands Journal of Sea Research* 3, 391-422.

DRAL, A.D.G. (1977). Regulation of the branchial ciliary activity in the mussel *Mytilus edulis* L. *Interne Verslagen Nederlands Institut voor Onderzoek der Zee*, Texel 1977(6), 1-24.

DRINNAN, R.E. (1964). An apparatus for recording the water-pumping behaviour of lamellibranchs. *Netherlands Journal of Sea Research* 2, 223-232.

DUBOS, R. (1965). Man Adapting. Yale University Press, New Haven.

DUNBAR, M.J. (1980). The blunting of Occam's Razor, or to hell with parsemony. *Canadian Journal of Zoology* 58, 123-128.

EPIFANIO, C.E. & EWART, J. (1977). Maximum ration of four diets for the oyster *Crassostrea virginica* Gmelin. *Aquaculture* 11, 13-29.

ESHLEMAN, W.P. & WILKENS, J.L. (1979). Brachiopod orientation to current direction and substrate position (*Terebratalia transversa*). *Canadian Journal of Zoology* 57, 2079-2082.

FAMME, P. (1981). Haemolymph circulation as a respiratory parameter in the mussel *Mytilus edulis* L. *Comparative Biochemistry and Physiology* 69A, 243-247.

FAMME, P. & KOFOED, L.H. (1980). The ventilatory current and ctenidial function related to oxygen uptake in declining oxygen tension by the mussel *Mytilus edulis* L. *Comparative Biochemistry and Physiology* 66A, 161-171.

FAMME, P., KNUDSEN, J. & HANSEN, E.S. (1981). The effect of oxygen on the aerobic-anaerobic metabolism of the marine bivalve, *Mytilus edulis* L. *Marine Biology Letters* 2, 345-351.

FAMME, P., RIISGÅRD, H.U. & JØRGENSEN, C.B. (1986). On direct measurements of pumping rates in the mussel *Mytilus edulis*. *Marine Biology* 92, 323-327.

FANKBONER, P.V. (1971). The ciliary currents associated with feeding, digestion, and sediment removal in *Adula (Botula) falcata* Gould 1851. *Biological Bulletin of the Marine Biological Laboratory, Woods Hole* 140, 28-45.

FEIBLEMAN, J. (1954-55). Theory of integrative levels. *The British Journal for the Philosophy of Science* 5, 59-66.

FENCHEL, T. (1980). Suspension feeding in ciliated protozoa: structure and function of feeding organelles. *Archiv für Protistenkunde* 123, 239-260.

FENCHEL, T. (1986). Protozoan filter feeding. *Progress in Protistology* 1, 65-113.

FENCHEL, T. & FINLAY, B.J. (1983). Respiration rates in heterotrophic, free-living Protozoa. *Microbial Ecology* 9, 99-122.

FJERDINGSTAD, E.J. (1961). The ultrastructure of choanocyte collars in *Spongilla lacustris* (L). *Zeitschrift für Zellforschung* 53, 645-657.

FOSTER-SMITH, R.L. (1975). The role of mucus in the mechanism of feeding in three filter-feeding bivalves. *Proceedings of the Malacological Society, London* 41, 571-588.

FOSTER-SMITH, R.L. (1976). Pressures generated by the pumping mechanism of some ciliary filter-feeders. *Journal of Experimental Marine Biology and Ecology* 25, 199-206.

REFERENCES

FOSTER-SMITH, R.L. (1978). The function of the pallial organs of bivalves in controlling ingestion. *Journal of Molluscan Studies* 44, 83-99.

FOX, D.L., SVERDRUP, H.N. & CUNNINGHAM, J.P. (1937). The rate of water propulsion by the California mussel. *Biological Bulletin of the Marine Biological Laboratory, Woods Hole* 72, 417-438.

FRÉCHETTE, M. & BOURGET, E. (1985a). Energy flow between the pelagic and benthic zones: Factors controlling particulate organic matter available to an intertidal mussel bed. *Canadian Journal of Fishery and Aquatic Sciences* 42, 1158-1165.

FRÉCHETTE, M. & BOURGET, E. (1985b). Food-limited growth of *Mytilus edulis* L. in relation to the benthic boundary layer. *Canadian Journal of Fishery and Aquatic Sciences* 42, 1166-1170.

FRÉCHETTE, M., BUTMAN, C.A. & GEYER, W.R. (1989). The importance of boundary-layer flows in supplying phytoplankton to the benthic suspension feeder, *Mytilus edulis* L. *Limnology and Oceanography* 37, 19-36.

FRETTER, V. & MONTGOMERY, M.C. (1968). The treatment of food by prosobranch veligers. *Journal of the Marine Biological Association of the United Kingdom* 48, 499-520.

FULLER, J.L. (1937). Feeding rate of *Calanus finmarchicus* in relation to environmental conditions. *Biological Bulletin of the Marine Biological Laboratory, Woods Hole* 72, 233-246.

GAFFNEY, P.M. & DIEHL, W.J. (1986). Growth, condition and specific dynamic action of the mussel *Mytilus edulis* recovering from starvation. *Marine Biology* 93, 401-409.

GALLAGER, S.M. (1988). Visual observations of particle manipulation during feeding in larvae of a bivalve mollusc. *Bulletin of Marine Science* 43, 344-365.

GALLAGER, S.M. & MANN, R. (1980). An apparatus for the measurement of grazing activity of filter feeders at constant food concentrations. *Marine Biology Letters* 1, 341-349.

GALTSOFF, P.S. (1946). Reaction of oysters to chlorination. *United States Fish and Wildlife Service, Research Report* 11.

GEORGE, S.G., CARPENE, E., COOMBS, T.L., OVERNELL, J. & YOUNGSON, A. (1979). Characterisation of cadmium-binding proteins from mussels, *Mytilus edulis* (L), exposed to cadmium. *Biochimica et Biophysica Acta* 580, 225-233.

GERDES, D. (1983). The pacific oyster *Crassostrea gigas*. Part 1. Feeding behaviour of larvae and adults. *Aquaculture* 31, 195-219.

GILMOUR, T.H.J. (1979). Feeding in pterobranch hemichordates and the evolution of gill slits. *Canadian Journal of Zoology* 57, 1136-1142.

GOLDBERG, E.D. (1975). The mussel watch – a first step in global marine monitoring. *Marine Pollution Bulletin* 6, 111.

GOLDBERG, E.D. (ed). (1976). Strategies for Marine Pollution Monitoring. Wiley, New York.

GOLDSTEIN, K. (1939). The Organism. American Book Company, New York.

GORHAM, W.T. (1988). The energetic and nutritional contribution of glucose and glycine taken up from natural sea water by adult marine mussels. *Marine Ecology* 9, 1-14.

GOSSELIN, R. (1961). The cilioexcitatory activity of serotonin. *Journal of Cellular and Comparative Physiology* 58, 17-26.

GOSSELIN, R.E. & O'HARA, C. (1961). An unsuspected source of error in studies of particle transport by lamellibranch gill cilia. *Journal of Cellular and Comparative Physiology* 58, 1-9.

GOSSELIN, R.E., MOORE, K.E. & MILTON, A.S. (1962). Physiological control of molluscan gill cilia by 5-hydroxytryptamine. *Journal of General Physiology* 46, 277-296.

GOULD, S.J. (1966). Allometry and size in ontogeny and phylogeny. *Biological Reviews* 41, 587-640.

GOULD, S.J. & LEWONTIN, R.C. (1979). The spandrels of San Marco and the Panglossian paradigm: a critique of the adaptationist programme. *Proceedings of the Royal Society, London* B 205, 581-598.

GOULD, S.J. & VRBA, E.S. (1982). Exaptation – a missing term in the science of form. *Paleobiology* 8, 4-15.

GRAHAM, A. (1931). On the morphology, feeding mechanisms, and digestion of *Ensis siliqua* (Schumacher). *Transactions of the Royal Society, Edinburgh* 56, 725-751.

GRAY, J. (1928). Ciliary Movement. Cambridge University Press, London.

GRAY, J. (1929). The mechanism of ciliary movement. *American Naturalist* 63, 68-81.

GRAY, J. (1930). The mechanism of ciliary movement. VI. Photographic and stroboscopic analysis of ciliary movement. *Proceedings of the Royal Society, London* B 107, 313-332.

GRENON, J.-F. & WALKER, G. (1980). Biochemical and rheological properties of the pedal mucus of the limpet, *Patella vulgata* L. *Comparative Biochemistry and Physiology* 66B, 451-458.

GRODZINSKI, W., KLEKOWSKI, R.Z. & DUNCAN, A. (eds.) (1975). Methods for Ecological Bioenergetics. IBP Handbook No 24. Blackwell, Oxford.

GRY, H. (1942). Das Wattenmeer bei Skallingen. No. 1. Quantitative Untersuchungen über den Sinkstofftransport durch Gezeitenströmungen. *Folia geographica Danica* 11, No. 1, 1-138.

HALFON, E. (ed.) (1979). Theoretical Systems Ecology: Advances and Case Studies. Academic Press, New York.

HAMBURGER, K., MØHLENBERG, F., RANDLØV, A. & RIISGÅRD, H.U. (1983). Size, oxygen consumption and growth in the mussel *Mytilus edulis*. *Marine Biology* 75, 303-306.

HARGER, J.R.E. (1970). Comparisons among growth characteristics of two species of sea mussel, *Mytilus edulis* and *Mytilus californianus*. *The Veliger* 13, 44-56.

HARTNOLL, R.G. (1967). An investigation of the movement of the scallop, *Pecten maximus*. *Helgoländer wissenschaftliche Meeresuntersuchungen* 15, 523-533.

HARVEY, H.W. (1937). Note on selective feeding by *Calanus*. *Journal of the Marine Biological Association of the United Kingdom* 22, 97-100.

HAVEN, D.S. & MORALES-ALAMO, R. (1966). Aspects of biodeposition by oysters and other invertebrate filter feeders. *Limnology and Oceanography* 11, 487-498.

HAVEN, D.S. & MORALES-ALAMO, R. (1970). Filtration of particles from suspension by the American oyster *Crassostrea virginica*. *Biological Bulletin of the Marine Biological Laboratory, Woods Hole* 139, 248-264.

HAVINGA, B. (1954). Hydrografie van het IJsselmeer. *In* Veranderingen in de Flora en Fauna van de Zuiderzee (ed. L.F. de Beaufort), pp. 1-24. De Boer, Den Helder.

REFERENCES

HAWKINS, A.J.S. & BAYNE, B.L. (1984). Seasonal variation in the balance between physiological mechanisms of feeding and digestion in *Mytilus edulis* (Bivalvia: Mollusca). *Marine Biology* 82, 233-240.

HAWKINS, A.J.S. & BAYNE, B.L. (1985). Seasonal variation in the relative utilization of carbon and nitrogen by the mussel *Mytilus edulis*: budgets, conversion efficiencies and maintenance requirements. *Marine Ecology Progress Series* 25, 181-188.

HAWKINS, A.J.S., BAYNE, B.L. & CLARKE, K.R. (1983). Co-ordinated rhythms of digestion, absorption and excretion in *Mytilus edulis* (Bivalvia: Mollusca). *Marine Biology* 74, 41-48.

HAWKINS, A.J.S., WIDDOWS, J. & BAYNE, B.L. (1989). The relevance of whole-body protein metabolism to measured costs of maintenance and growth in *Mytilus edulis*. *Physiological Zoology* 62, 745-763.

HAWKINS, A.J.S., SALKELD, P.N., BAYNE, B.L., GNAIGER, E. & LOWE, D.M. (1985). Feeding and resource allocation in the mussel *Mytilus edulis*: evidence for time-averaged optimization. *Marine Ecology Progress Series* 20, 273-287.

HERDMAN, W.A. (1904). Ceylon Pearl Oyster Fisheries and Marine Biology. Part II. Royal Society, London.

HILDRETH, D.I. (1976). The influence of water flow rate on pumping rate in *Mytilus edulis* using a refined direct measurement apparatus. *Journal of the Marine Biological Association of the United Kingdom* 56, 311-319.

HILDRETH, D.I. & CRISP, D.J. (1976). A corrected formula for calculation of filtration rate of bivalve molluscs in an experimental flowing system. *Journal of the Marine Biological Association of the United Kingdom* 56, 111-120.

HIRATA, T., KUBOTA, I., IMADA, M. & MUNEOKA, Y. (1989a). Phamacology of relaxing response of *Mytilus* smooth muscle to the catch-relaxing peptide. *Comparative Biochemistry and Physiology* 92C, 289-295.

HIRATA, T., KUBOTA, I., IMADA, M., MUNEOKA, Y. & KOBAYASHI, M. (1989b). Effects of the catch-relaxing peptide on molluscan muscles. *Comparative Biochemistry and Physiology* 92C, 283-288.

HOWELL, R., GRANT, A.M. & MACCOY, N.E.J. (1984). Effect of treatment with reserpine on the change in filtration rate of *Mytilus edulis* subjected to dissolved copper. *Marine Pollution Bulletin* 15, 436-439.

HUGHES, R.N. (ed.) (1990). Behavioural Mechanisms of Food Selection. *NATO ASI Series*: Subseries G 'Ecological Sciences', Springer-Verlag, Heidelberg, New York.

HUGHES, T.G. (1975). The sorting of food particles by *Abra* sp. (Bivalvia: Tellinacea). *Journal of Experimental Marine Biology and Ecology* 20, 137-156.

IVLEV, V.S. (1945). The biological productivity of water. *Translation Series of Journal of Fishery Research Board of Canada* 23, 1727-1759, 1965.

JACKSON, G.A. (1980). Phytoplankton growth and zooplankton grazing in oligotrophic oceans. *Nature* 284, 439-441.

JACOB, F. (1976). The Logic of Life. Vintage Books, New York.

JANSSEN, H.H. & SCHOLZ, N. (1979). Uptake and cellular distribution of cadmium in *Mytilus edulis*. *Marine Biology* 55, 133-141.

JANSSENS, F. (1893). Les branchies des Acéphales. *La Cellule* 9, 1-118.

[*121*]

JANSSON, A.-M. & KAUTSKY, N. (1977). Quantitative survey of hard bottom communities in a Baltic archipelago. *In* Biology of Benthic Organisms (eds. B.F. Keegan, P. O'Céidigh & P.J.S. Boaden), pp 359-366. Pergamon Press, Oxford.

JOBLING, M. (1983). A short review and critique of methodology used in fish growth and nutrition studies. *Journal of Fish Biology* 23, 685-703.

JOBLING, M. (1985). Growth. *In* Fish Energetics: New Perspectives (eds. P. Tytler & P. Calow), pp. 213-230. Croom Helm, London.

JØRGENSEN, B.B. (1980). Seasonal oxygen depletion in the bottom waters of a Danish fjord and its effect on the benthic community. *Oikos* 34, 68-76.

JØRGENSEN, C.B. (1943). On the water transport through the gills of bivalves. *Acta physiologica Scandinavica* 5, 297-304.

JØRGENSEN, C.B. (1949). The rate of feeding by *Mytilus* in different kinds of suspension. *Journal of the Marine Biological Association of the United Kingdom* 28, 333-344.

JØRGENSEN, C.B. (1952). Efficiency of growth in *Mytilus edulis* and two gastropod veligers. *Nature,* London 170, 714.

JØRGENSEN, C.B. (1955). Quantitative aspects of filter feeding in invertebrates. *Biological Reviews* 30, 391-454.

JØRGENSEN, C.B. (1966). Biology of Suspension Feeding. Pergamon Press, Oxford.

JØRGENSEN, C.B. (1975a). On gill function in the mussel *Mytilus edulis* L. *Ophelia* 13, 187-232.

JØRGENSEN, C.B. (1975b). Comparative physiology of suspension feeding. *Annual Review of Physiology* 37, 57-79.

JØRGENSEN, C.B. (1976a) Comparative studies on the function of gills in suspension feeding bivalves, with special reference to effects of serotonin. *Biological Bulletin of the Marine Biological Laboratory, Woods Hole* 151, 331-343.

JØRGENSEN, C.B. (1976b). Growth efficiencies and factors controlling size in some mytilid bivalves, especially *Mytilus edulis:* review and interpretation. *Ophelia* 15, 175-192.

JØRGENSEN, C.B. (1981a). A hydromechanical principle for particle retention in *Mytilus edulis* and other ciliary suspension feeders. *Marine Biology* 61, 277-282.

JØRGENSEN, C.B. (1981b). Feeding and cleaning mechanisms in the suspension feeding bivalve *Mytilus edulis. Marine Biology* 65, 159-163.

JØRGENSEN, C.B. (1981c). Mortality, growth, and grazing impact of a cohort of bivalve larvae, *Mytilus edulis* L. *Ophelia* 20, 185-192.

JØRGENSEN, C.B. (1982). Fluid mechanics of the mussel gill: the lateral cilia. *Marine Biology* 70, 275-281.

JØRGENSEN, C.B. (1983a). Fluid mechanical aspects of suspension feeding. *Marine Ecology Progress Series* 11, 89-103.

JØRGENSEN, C.B. (1983b). Patterns of uptake of dissolved amino acids in mussels (*Mytilus edulis*). *Marine Biology* 73, 177-182.

JØRGENSEN, C.B. (1983c). Ecological physiology: Background and perspectives. *Comparative Biochemistry and Physiology* 75A, 5-7.

JØRGENSEN, C.B. (1984). Effect of grazing: metazoan suspension feeders. *In* Heterotrophic Activity in the Sea (eds. J.E. Hobbie & P.J. le B. Williams), pp 445-464. Plenum Press, New York.

[122]

REFERENCES

JØRGENSEN, C.B. (1988). Metabolic costs of growth and maintenance in the toad, *Bufo bufo*. *Journal of Experimental Biology* 138, 319-331.

JØRGENSEN, C.B. (1989). Water processing in ciliary feeders, with special reference to the bivalve filter pump. *Comparative Biochemstry and Physiology* 94A, 383-394.

JØRGENSEN, C.B. (1990a). Water processing in filter-feeding bivalves. *In* Behavioural Mechanisms of Food Selection (ed. R.N. Hughes). *NATO ASI Series*, Subseries G 'Ecological Sciences', 615-636. Springer-Verlag, Heidelberg, New York.

JØRGENSEN, C.B. (1990b). Adaptational, environmental and ecological physiology: A case for hierarchical thinking. *In* Strategies of Physiological Adaptation (ed. C. Lenfant). Marcel Dekker, New York, in press.

JØRGENSEN, C.B. & GOLDBERG, E.D. (1953). Particle filtration in some ascidians and lamellibranchs. *Biological Bulletin of the Marine Biological Laboratory, Woods Hole* 105, 477-489.

JØRGENSEN, C.B. & OCKELMANN, K. (1990). Beat frequency of lateral cilia in intact filter feeding bivalves: Effect of temperature. *Ophelia*, in press.

JØRGENSEN, C.B. & RIISGÅRD, H.U. (1988). Gill pump characteristics of the soft clam *Mya arenaria*. *Marine Biology* 99, 107-109.

JØRGENSEN, C.B., LARSEN, P.S. & RIISGÅRD, H.U. (1990). Effects of temperature on the mussel pump. *Marine Ecology Progress Series*, 64, 89-97.

JØRGENSEN, C.B., MØHLENBERG, F. & STEN-KNUDSEN, O. (1986a). Nature of relation between ventilation and oxygen consumption in filter feeders. *Marine Ecology Progress Series* 29, 73-88.

JØRGENSEN, C.B., KIØRBOE, T., MØHLENBERG, F. & RIISGÅRD, H.U. (1984). Ciliary and mucus-net filter feeding, with special reference to fluid mechanical characteristics. *Marine Ecology Progress Series* 15, 283-292.

JØRGENSEN, C.B., LARSEN, P.S., MØHLENBERG, F. & RIISGÅRD, H.U. (1988). The bivalve pump: properties and modelling. *Marine Ecology Progress Series*, 45, 205-216.

JØRGENSEN, C.B., FAMME, P., KRISTENSEN, H.S., LARSEN, P.S., MØHLENBERG, F. & RIISGÅRD, H.U. (1986b). The bivalve pump. *Marine Ecology Progress Series* 34, 69-77.

JONES, A.M. (1979). Structure and growth of a high-level population of *Cerastoderma edule* (Lamellibranchia). *Journal of the Marine Biological Association of the United Kingdom* 59, 277-287.

JONES, H.D. & ALLEN, J.R. (1986). Inhalant and exhalant pressures in *Mytilus edulis* L. and *Cerastoderma edule* (L.). *Journal of Experimental Marine Biology and Ecology* 98, 231-240.

JORDAN, T.E. & VALIELA, I. (1982). A nitrogen budget of the ribbed mussel, *Geukensia demissa*, and its significance in nitrogen flow in a New England salt marsh. *Limnology and Oceanography* 27, 75-90.

JUDD, W. (1971). The structure and habits of *Divariscintilla maoria* Powell (Bivalvia: Galeommatidae). *Proceedings of the Malacological Society, London* 39, 343-353.

KAUTSKY, N. & EVANS, S. (1987). Role of biodeposition by *Mytilus edulis* in the circulation of matter and nutrients in a Baltic coastal ecosystem. *Marine Ecology Progress Series* 38, 201-212.

[*123*]

KELLOGG, J.L. (1892). A contribution to our knowledge of the morphology of lamellibranchiate mollusks. *Bulletin of the United States Fishery Commission* 10, 389-436.

KELLOGG, J.L. (1915). Ciliary mechanisms of lamellibranchs with descriptions of anatomy. *Journal of Morphology* 26, 625-701.

KIØRBOE, T. (1988). Planktonfødekæden: Bioenergetiske og økologiske studier. *Danmarks Fiskeri- og Havundersøgelser.*

KIØRBOE, T. & MØHLENBERG, F. (1981). Particle selection in suspension-feeding bivalves. *Marine Ecology Progress Series* 5, 291-296.

KIØRBOE, T. & MØHLENBERG, F. (1987). Partitioning of oxygen consumption between 'maintenance' and 'growth' in developing herring *Clupea harengus* (L.) embryos. *Journal of Experimental Marine Biology and Ecology* 111, 99-108.

KIØRBOE, T., MØHLENBERG, F. & NØHR, O. (1980). Feeding, particle selection and carbon absorption in *Mytilus edulis* in different mixtures of algae and resuspended bottom material. *Ophelia* 19, 193-205.

KIØRBOE, T., MØHLENBERG, F. & NØHR, O. (1981). Effect of suspended bottom material on growth and energetics in *Mytilus edulis*. *Marine Biology* 61, 283-288.

KIØRBOE, T., MUNK, P. & RICHARDSON, K. (1987). Respiration and growth of larval herring *Clupea harengus*: relation between specific dynamic action and growth efficiency. *Marine Ecology Progress Series* 40, 1-10.

KNIGHT-JONES, E.W. (1954). Relations between metachronism and the direction of ciliary beat in Metazoa. *Quarterly Journal of Microscopical Science* 95, 503-521.

KÖHLER, K. & RIISGÅRD, H.U. (1982). Formation of metallothioneins in relation to accumulation of cadmium in the common mussel *Mytilus edulis*. *Marine Biology* 66, 53-58.

KOESTLER, A. & SMYTHIES, J.R. (eds.) (1969). Beyond Reductionism. Hutchinson, London.

KRISTENSEN, J.H. (1972). Structure and function of crystalline style of bivalves. *Ophelia* 10, 91-108.

KRYGER, J. & RIISGÅRD, H.U. (1988). Filtration rate capacities in 6 species of European freshwater bivalves. *Oecologia* 77, 34-38.

KUENZLER, E.J. (1961). Phosphorus budget of a mussel population. *Limnology and Oceanography* 6, 400-415.

LABARBERA, M. (1977). Brachiopod orientation to water movement. I. Theory, laboratory behavior, and field orientation. *Paleobiology* 3, 270-287.

LABARBERA, M. (1981). Water flow patterns in and around three species of articulate brachiopods. *Journal of Experimental Marine Biology and Ecology* 55, 185-206.

LABARBERA, M. (1984). Feeding currents and particle capture mechanisms in suspension feeding animals. *American Zoologist* 24, 71-84.

LAM, V.W.W. (1977). Shell form and diagnostic differences in the structure of the siphons and ciliary currents of the ctenidia in coastal species of the Tapetinae (Bivalvia: Veneracea) in Hong Kong. *Proceedings I. International Workshop on the Malacofauna of Hong Kong and Southern China* 1977, pp 11-31. Hong Kong.

LANDE, E. (1973). Growth, spawning, and mortality of the mussel (*Mytilus edulis* L.) in Prestvaagen, Trondheimsfjorden. *Kongelige Norske Videnskabers Selskab, Museet. Miscellanea* 11, 1-26.

REFERENCES

LARKIN, P.A. (1977). An epitaph for the concept of maximum sustained yield. *Transactions of the American Fisheries Society* 106, 1-11.

LASHLEY, K.S. (1929). Brain Mechanisms and Intelligence. Chicago University Press, Chicago.

LEAL, L.G. (1980). Particle motions in a viscous fluid. *Annual Review of Fluid Mechanics* 12, 435-476.

LIST, T. (1902). Die Mytiliden des Golfes von Neapel und der angrenzenden Meeres-Abschnitte. Friedländer, Berlin.

LITT, M. (1971). Flow behavior of mucus. *Annals of Otology* 80, 330-335.

LONGHURST, A.R. (1976). Interactions between zooplankton and phytoplankton profiles in the eastern tropical Pacific Ocean. *Deep-Sea Research* 23, 729-754.

LOO, L.-O. & ROSENBERG, R. (1983). *Mytilus edulis* culture: growth and production in Western Sweden. *Aquaculture* 35, 137-150.

LOO, L.-O. & ROSENBERG, R. (1989). Bivalve suspension-feeding dynamics and benthic-pelagic coupling in an eutrophicated marine bay. *Journal of Experimental Marine Biology and Ecology* 130, 253-276.

LOOSANOFF, V.L. (1958). Some aspects of behavior of oysters at different temperatures. *Biological Bulletin of the Marine Biological Laboratory, Woods Hole* 114, 57-70.

LOOSANOFF, V.L. & ENGLE, J.B. (1947). Effect of different concentrations of micro-organisms on the feeding of oysters (*O. virginica*). *Fisheries Bulletin, United States* 51, 31-57.

LUCAS, M.I., NEWELL, R.C. SHUMWAY, S.E., SEIDERER, L.J. & BALLY, R. (1987). Particle clearance and yield in relation to bacterioplankton and suspended particulate availability in estuarine and open coast populations of the mussel *Mytilus edulis*. *Marine Ecology Progress Series* 36, 215-224.

LUND, E.J. (1957). Self-silting of the oyster and its significance for sedimentation geology. *Institute of Marine Sciences* 4, 320-327.

McCAMMON, H.M. (1971). Behavior in the brachiopod *Terebratulina septemtrionalis* (Couthony). *Journal of Experimental Marine Biology and Ecology* 6, 35-45.

McCAULEY, E. & BRIAND, F. (1979). Zooplankton grazing and phytoplankton species richness: Field tests of the predation hypothesis. *Limnology and Oceanography* 24, 243-252.

MacGINITIE, G.E. (1941). On the method of feeding in four Pelecypods. *Biological Bulletin of the Marine Biological Laboratory, Woods Hole* 80, 18-25.

MACHEMER, H. (1974). Ciliary activity and metachronism in Protozoa. *In* Cilia and Flagella (ed. M.A. Sleigh), pp. 199-286. Academic Press, London.

MANAHAN, D.T., WRIGHT, S.H. & STEPHENS, G.C. (1983). Simultaneous determination of net uptake of 16 amino acids by a marine bivalve. *American Journal of Physiology* 244 (Regulatory Integrative Comparative Physiology 13) R832-R838.

MASON, J. (1976). Cultivation. *In* Marine Mussels: Their Ecology and Physiology (ed. B.L. Bayne), pp 385-410. Cambridge University Press, Cambridge.

MAYR, E. (1982). Evolution of Biological Thought. Belknap Press, Cambridge, Mass.

MEDAWAR, P.A. (1967). The Art of the Soluble. Methuen, London.

[*125*]

MERZ, R.A. (1984). Self-generated *versus* environmentally produced feeding currents: a comparison for the sabellid polychaete *Eudistylia vancouveri*. Biological Bulletin of the Marine Biological Laboratory, Woods Hole 167, 200-209.

MEYHÖFER, E. (1985). Comparative pumping rates in suspension-feeding bivalves. Marine Biology 85, 137-142.

MILLAR, R.H. (1955). Notes on the mechanism of food movement in the gut of the larval oyster, *Ostrea edulis*. Quarterly Journal of Microscopical Science 96, 539-544.

MØHLENBERG, F. & ANDERSEN, F. (1987). Kviksølvkoncentration i naturligt forekommende muslinger, samt optagelse af kviksølv i transplanterede blåmuslinger i Københavns havn. Report from the Marine Pollution Laboratory, Copenhagen.

MØHLENBERG, F. & KIØRBOE, T. (1981). Growth and energetics in *Spisula subtruncata* (Da Costa) and the effect of suspended bottom material. Ophelia 20, 79-90.

MØHLENBERG, F. & RIISGÅRD, H.U. (1978). Efficiency of particle retention in 13 species of suspension feeding bivalves. Ophelia 17, 239-246.

MØHLENBERG, F. & RIISGÅRD, H.U. (1979). Filtration rate, using a new indirect technique, in thirteen species of suspension-feeding bivalves. Marine Biology 54, 143-148.

MOHRI, H. (1956). Studies on the respiration of sea-urchin spermatozoa. I. The effect of 2,4-dinitrophenol and sodium azide. Journal of Experimental Biology 33, 73-81.

MOORE, H.J. (1971). The structure of the latero-frontal cirri on the gills of certain lamellibranch molluscs and their role in suspension feeding. Marine Biology 11, 23-27.

MORTON, B. (1969). Studies on the biology of *Dreissena polymorpha* Pall. I. General anatomy and morphology. Proceedings of the Malacological Society, London 38, 301-321.

MORTON, B. (1970). The functional anatomy of the organs of feeding and digestion of *Teredo navalis* Linnaeus and *Lyrodus pedicellatus* (Quatrefages). Proceedings of the Malacological Society, London 39, 151-167.

MORTON, B. (1976). The biology, ecology and functional aspects of the organs of feeding and digestion of the S.E. Asian mangrove bivalve, *Enigmonia aenigmatica* (Mollusca: Anomiacea). Journal of Zoology, London 179, 437-466.

MORTON, B. (1983). Feeding and digestion in Bivalvia. *In* The Mollusca (ed. K.M. Wilbur), Vol. 5, pp. 65-147.

MORTON, J.E. (1960). The functions of the gut in ciliary feeders. Biological Reviews 35, 92-140.

MORTON, J.E. (1967). Guts. Arnold, London.

MUNEOKA, Y. & KAMURA, M. (1982). The multiplicity of neurotransmitters and neurohormones controlling *Mytilus* muscle. Comparative Biochemistry and Physiology 73C, 149-156.

MURAKAMI, A. (1987a). Control of ciliary beat frequency in the gill of *Mytilus*. – I. Activation of the lateral cilia by cyclic AMP. Comparative Biochemistry and Physiology 86C, 273-279.

MURAKAMI, A. (1987b). Control of ciliary beat frequency in the gill of *Mytilus* – II. Effects of saponin and Brij-58 on the lateral cilia. Comparative Biochemistry and Physiology 86C, 281-287.

MURAKAMI, A. (1989). The control of cilia in metazoa: Ciliary functions and Ca-dependent responses. Comparative Biochemistry and Physiology 94A, 375-382.

REFERENCES

NARCHI, W. (1972). On the biology of *Iphigenia brasiliensis* Lamarck, 1818 (Bivalvia, Donacidae). *Proceedings of the Malacological Society, London* 40, 79-91.

NAVARRO, J.M. & WINTER, J.E. (1982). Ingestion rate, assimilation efficiency and energy balance in *Mytilus chilensis* in relation to body size and different algal concentrations. *Marine Biology* 67, 255-266.

NELSON, T.C. (1935). Water filtration by the oyster and a new hormone effect thereon. *Anatomical Record* 64, Supplement 1, 68.

NELSON, T.C. (1960). The feeding mechanism of the oyster. II. On the gills and palps of *Ostrea edulis, Crassostrea virginica* and *C. angulata. Journal of Morphology* 107, 163-203.

NEWELL, R.C. (1970). Biology of Intertidal Animals. Logos, London.

NEWELL, R.C. & BAYNE, B.L. (1980). Seasonal changes in the physiology, reproductive condition and carbohydrate content of the cockle *Cardium* (= *Cerastoderma*) *edule* (Bivalvia: Cardiidae). *Marine Biology* 56, 11-19.

NEWELL, R.C. & BRANCH, G.M. (1980). The influence of temperature on the maintenance of metabolic energy balance in marine invertebrates. *Advances in Marine Biology* 17, 329-396.

NEWELL, R.C. & KOFOED, L.H. (1977). The energetics of suspension-feeding in the gastropod *Crepidula fornicata* L. *Journal of the Marine Biological Association of the United Kingdom* 51, 161-180.

NEWELL, R.C. & PYE, V.J. (1970). Seasonal changes in the effect of temperature on the oxygen consumption of the winkle *Littorina littorea* (L.) and the mussel *Mytilus edulis* (L.). *Comparative Biochemistry and Physiology* 34, 367-383.

NEWELL, R.C., JOHNSON, L.G. & KOFOED, L.H. (1977). Adjustment of the components of energy balance in response to temperature change in *Ostrea edulis. Oecologia* 30, 97-110.

NEWELL, R.I.E. & JORDAN, S.J. (1983). Preferential ingestion of organic material by the American oyster *Crassostrea virginica. Marine Ecology Progress Series* 13, 47-53.

NICOL, E.A.T. (1931). The feeding mechanism, formation of the tube, and physiology of digestion in *Sabella pavonina. Transactions of the Royal Society of Edinburgh* 56, 537-598.

NICOLAJSEN, H., MØHLENBERG, F. & KIØRBOE, T. (1983). Algal grazing by the planktonic copepods *Centropages hamatus* and *Pseudocalanus* sp.: diurnal and seasonal variation during the spring phytoplankton bloom in the Øresund. *Ophelia* 22, 15-31.

NIKLAS, K.J. (1985). Wind pollination – a study in controlled chaos. *American Scientist* 73, 462-470.

NOVIKOFF, A.B. (1945). The concept of integrative levels and biology. *Science* 101, 209-215.

OFFICER, C.B., SMAYDA, T.J. & MANN, R. (1982). Benthic filter feeding: a natural eutrophication control. *Marine Ecology Progress Series* 9, 203-210.

ORTON, J.H. (1912). The mode of feeding of *Crepidula*, with an account of the current-producing mechanism in the mantle cavity, and some remarks on the mode of feeding in Gastropods and Lamellibranchs. *Journal of the Marine Biological Association of the United Kingdom* 9, 444-478.

OWEN, G. (1953). On the biology of *Glossus humanus* (L.) (*Isocardia cor* Lam.). *Journal of the Marine Biological Association of the United Kingdom* 32, 85-106.

OWEN, G. (1974a). Studies on the gill of *Mytilus edulis*: the eu-latero-frontal cirri. *Proceedings of the Royal Society of London*, Series B. 187, 83-91.

OWEN, G. (1974b). Feeding and digestion in the bivalvia. *Advances in Comparative Physiology and Biochemistry* 5, 1-35.

OWEN, G. & MCCRAE, J.M. (1976). Further studies on the latero-frontal tract of bivalves. *Proceedings of the Malacological Society, London* B. 194, 527-544.

PALMER, R.E. (1980). Behavioral and rhythmic aspects of filtration in the bay scallop, *Argopecten irradians concentricus* (Say), and the oyster, *Crassostrea virginica* (Gmelin). *Journal of Experimental Marine Biology and Ecology* 45, 273-295.

PALMER, R.E. & WILLIAMS, L.G. (1980), Effect of particle concentrations on filtration efficiency of the bay scallop *Argopecten irradians* and the oyster *Crassostrea virginica*. *Ophelia* 19, 163-174.

PAPARO, A.A. (1985). The role of the cerebral and visceral ganglia in ciliary activity. *Comparative Biochemistry and Physiology* 81A, 647-651.

PAPARO, A.A. (1986a). Cilioinhibitory process initiated by a neuronal pigment in *Crassostrea virginica*. *Comparative Biochemistry and Physiology* 84a, 299-302.

PAPARO, A.A. (1986b). Neuroregulatory activities and potassium enhancement of lateral ctenidial beating in *Crassostrea virginica*. *Comparative Biochemistry and Physiology* 84A, 585-588.

PAPARO, A.A. (1988). Ciliary activity on the ctenidium of bivalve molluscs. *Comparative Biochemistry and Physiology* 91C, 99-110.

PATTEE, H.H. (1970). The problem of biological hierarchy. *In* Towards a Theoretical Biology. 3. Drafts, (ed. C.H. Waddington), pp. 117-136. Edinburgh University Press, Edinburgh.

PATTEE, H.H. (ed.) (1973). Hierarchy Theory: The Challenge of Complex Systems. Braziller, New York.

PAUL, A.J., PAUL, J.M. & NEVÉ, R.A. (1978). Phytoplankton densities and growth of *Mytilus edulis* in an Alaskan artificial upwelling system. *Journal du Conseil International pour l'Exploration de la Mer* 38, 100-104.

PELSENEER, P. (1906). Mollusca: The Lamellibranchia. *In* Lankester's Treatise of Zoology, Vol. 5, Chapter 5, pp. 205-284.

PHILLIPS, D.J.H. (1980). Quantitative Aquatic Biological Indicators. Applied Science Publishers, London.

PIANKA, E.R. (1978). Evolutionary Ecology (2.ed.). Harper & Row, New York.

POULSEN, E., RIISGÅRD, H.U. & MØHLENBERG, F. (1982). Accumulation of cadmium and bioenergetics in the mussel *Mytilus edulis*. *Marine Biology* 68, 25-29.

PROSSER, C.L. (1965). Levels of biological organization and their physiological significance. *In* Ideas in Modern Biology, (ed. John A. Moore), pp. 357-390. The Natural History Press, New York.

PURCELL, E.M. (1977). Life at low Reynolds number. *American Journal of Physics* 45, 3-11.

PURCHON, R.D. (1954). A note on the biology of the lamellibranch *Rocellaria* (*Gastrochaena*) *cuneformis* Spengler. *Proceedings of the Zoological Society, London* 124, 17-33.

PURCHON, R.D. (1955a). The functional morphology of the rock-boring lamellibranch *Petricola pholadiformis* Lamarck. *Journal of the Marine Biological Association of the United Kingdom* 34, 257-278.

PURCHON, R.D. (1955b). The structure and function of the British Pholadidae (rock-boring lamellibranchia). *Proceedings of the Zoological Society, London* 124, 859-911.

PYKE, G.H. (1984). Optimal foraging theory: a critical review. *Annual Review of Ecology and Systematics* 15, 523-575.

RAO, K.P. (1953). Rate of water propulsion in *Mytilus californianus. Biological Bulletin of the Marine Biological Laboratory, Woods Hole* 104, 171-181.

RAWSON, K.J & TUPPER, E.C. (1968). Basic Ship Theory. American Elsevier, New York.

REICH, D.J. (1964). Studies on *Mytilus edulis* community in Alamitos Bay, California: I. Development and destruction of the community. *The Veliger* 6, 124-131.

REID, L. (1970). Chronic bronchites – A report on mucus research. *Proceedings of the Royal Institution of Great Britain* 43, 438-463.

REID, R.G.B. (1965). The structure and function of the stomach in bivalve molluscs. *Journal of Zoology, London* 147, 156-184.

REISWIG, H.M. (1973). Population dynamics of three Jamaican demospongiae. *Bulletin of Marine Science* 23, 191-226.

REISWIG, H.M. (1974). Water transport, respiration and energetics of three tropical marine sponges. *Journal of Experimental Marine Biology and Ecology* 14, 231-249.

RIBELIN, B.W. & COLLIER, A. (1977). Studies on the gill ciliation of the American oyster *Crassostrea virginica* (Gmelin). *Journal of Morphology* 151, 439-449.

RIDEWOOD, W.G. (1903). On the structure of the gills of the Lamellibranchia. *Philosophical Transactions of the Royal Society, London Series* B 195, 147-284.

RIISGÅRD, H.U. (1977). On measurements of the filtration rates of suspension feeding bivalves in a flow system. *Ophelia* 16, 167-173.

RIISGÅRD, H.U. (1988a). Efficiency of particle retention and filtration rate in 6 species of Northeast American bivalves. *Marine Ecology Progress Series* 45, 217-223.

RIISGÅRD, H.U. (1988b). The ascidian pump: properties and energy cost. *Marine Ecology Progress Series* 47, 129-134.

RIISGÅRD, H.U. (1989). Properties and energy cost of the muscular piston pump in the suspension feeding polychaete *Chaetopterus variopedatus. Marine Ecology Progress Series* 56, 157-168.

RIISGÅRD, H.U. (1990). Filtration rate in the mussel *Mytilus edulis*: dependence on algal concentration. In manuscript.

RIISGÅRD, H.U. & MØHLENBERG, F. (1979). An improved automatic recording apparatus for determining the filtration rate of *Mytilus edulis* as a function of size and algal concentration. *Marine Biology* 52, 61-67.

RIISGÅRD, H.U. & POULSEN, E. (1981). Growth of *Mytilus edulis* in net bags transferred to different localities in a eutrophicated Danish fjord. *Marine Pollution Bulletin* 12, 272-276.

RIISGÅRD, H.U. & RANDLØV, A. (1981). Energy budgets, growth and filtration rates in *Mytilus edulis* at different algal concentrations. *Marine Biology* 61, 227-234.

RIISGÅRD, H.U., BJØRNESTAD, E. & MØHLENBERG, F. (1987). Accumulation of cadmium in the mussel *Mytilus edulis:* kinetics and importance of uptake via food and sea water. *Marine Biology* 96, 349-353.

RIISGÅRD, H.U., RANDLØV, A. & KRISTENSEN, P.S. (1980). Rates of water processing, oxygen consumption and efficiency of particle retention in veligers and young post-metamorphic *Mytilus edulis*. *Ophelia* 19, 37-46.

RIKMENSPOEL, R. (1984). Movements and active moments of bull sperm flagella as a function of temperature and viscosity. *Journal of Experimental Biology* 108, 205-230.

RIKMENSPOEL, R., SINTON, S. & JANICK, J.J. (1969). Energy conversion in bull sperm flagella. *Journal of General Physiology* 54, 782-805.

ROBINSON, W.E., WEHLING, W.E. & MORSE, H.P. (1984). The effect of suspended clay on feeding and digestive efficiency of the surf clam, *Spisula solidissima* (Dillwyn). *Journal of Experimental Marine Biology and Ecology* 74, 1-12.

RODHOUSE, P.G., MCDONALD, J.H., NEWELL, R.I.E. & KOEHN, R.K. (1986). Gamete production, somatic growth and multiple-locus enzyme heterozygosity in *Mytilus edulis*. *Marine Biology* 90, 209-214.

RODHOUSE, P.G., RODEN, C.M., BURNELL, G.M., HENSEY, M.P., MCMAHON, T., OTTWAY, B. & RYAN, T.H. (1984). Food resource, gametogenesis and growth of *Mytilus edulis* on the shore and in suspended culture: Killary Harbour, Ireland. *Journal of the Marine Biological Association of the United Kingdom* 64, 513-529.

RONKIN, R.R. (1955). Some physicochemical properties of mucus. *Archives of Biochemistry and Biophysics* 56, 76-89.

ROSS, D.H. & CRAIG, D.A. (1980). Mechanisms of fine particle capture by larval black flies (Diptera: Simuliidae). *Canadian Journal of Zoology* 58, 1186-1192.

ROTHCHILD, I. (1979). Ovarian follicular and corpus luteum function. *Advances in Experimental Medicine and Biology* 112, 767-789.

RUSSELL-HUNTER, W.D. (1979). A Life of Invertebrates. Macmillan, New York.

SALTHE, S.N. (1985). Evolving Hierarchical Systems. Columbia University Press, New York.

SANDERSON, M.J., DIRKSEN E.R. & SATIR, P. (1985). The antagonistic effects of 5-hydroxytryptamine and methylxanthine on the gill cilia of *Mytilus edulis*. *Cell Motility* 5, 293-309.

SANINA, L.V. (1976). Rate and intensity of filtration in some Caspian Sea bivalve molluscs. *Oceanology* (USSR) 15, 496-498.

SATIR, P. (1985). Switching mechanisms in the control of ciliary motility. *Modern Cell Biology* 4, 1-46.

SATIR, P. (1989). The role of axonemal components in ciliary motility. *Comparative Biochemistry and Physiology* 94A, 351-357.

SATIR, P., WAIS-STEIDER, J., LEBDUSKA, S., NASR, A. & AVOLIO, J. (1981). The mechanochemical cycle of the dynein arm. *Cell Motility* 1, 303-327.

SAWYER, L.J.E. (1972). A technique for recording the filtering activity of marine invertebrates. *Journal du Conseil International pour l'Exploration de la Mer* 34, 308-312.

SCHNEIRLA, T.C. (1941). Social organization in insects, as related to individual function. *The Psychological Review* 48, 465-486.

SCHULTE, E.H. (1975). Influence of algal concentration and temperature on the filtration rate of *Mytilus edulis*. *Marine Biology* 30, 331-341.

SEED, R. (1968). Factors influencing shell shape in the mussel *Mytilus edulis*. *Journal of the Marine Biological Association of the United Kingdom* 48, 561-584.

REFERENCES

SEED, R. (1969). The ecology of *Mytilus edulis* L. (Lamellibranchiata) on exposed rocky shores. II. Growth and mortality. *Oecologia* 3, 317-350.

SEGERDAHL, E. (1922). Investigations on the effect of a direct electric current on the ciliary motion of the *Anodonta* gill. *Skandinavisches Archiv für Physiologie* 42, 62-76.

SHARPEY, W. (1830). On a peculiar motion excited in fluids by the surfaces of certain animals. *Edinburgh Medical and Surgical Journal* 34, 113-122.

SHARPEY, W. (1836). Cilia. *In* The Cyclopædia of Anatomy and Physiology (ed. R.B. Todd), Vol. 1, 606-638.

SHELDON, R.W. & PARSONS, T.R. (1967). A Practical Manual on the Use of the Coulter Counter in Marine Science. Coulter Electronics Sales Company, Toronto, Canada.

SHUMWAY, S.E., CUCCI, R.C. & YENTSCH, C.M. (1985). Particle selection, ingestion, and absorption in filter-feeding bivalves. *Journal of Experimental Marine Biology and Ecology* 91, 77-92.

SHUMWAY, S.E., NEWELL, R.C., CRISP, D.J. & CUCCI, T.L. (1990). Particle selection in filter-feeding bivalve molluscs: a new technique on an old theme. *In* The Bivalvia. Proceedings of a Symposium in Memory of Sir Charles Maurice Yonge, Edinburgh, 1986. (ed. B. Morton). Hong Kong University Press, Hong Kong.

SIEBERS, D. & WINKLER, A. (1984). Amino-acid uptake by mussels, *Mytilus edulis*, from natural sea water in a flow-through system. *Helgoländer Meeresuntersuchungen* 38, 189-199.

SILVESTER, N.R. (1988). Hydrodynamics of flow in *Mytilus* gills. *Journal of Experimental Marine Biology and Ecology* 120, 171-182.

SILVESTER, N.R. & SLEIGH, M.A. (1984). Hydrodynamic aspects of particle capture by *Mytilus*. *Journal of the Marine Biological Association of the United Kingdom* 64, 859-879.

SIMKISS, K. & WILBUR, K.M. (1977). The molluscan epidermis and its secretions. *Symposia of the Zoological Society of London* 39, 35-76.

SIMON, H.A. (1962). The architecture of complexity. *Proceedings of the American Philosophical Society* 106, 467-482.

SLEIGH, M.A. & AIELLO, E. (1972). The movement of water by cilia. *Acta Protozoologica* 11, 265-277.

SMAAL, A.C., VERHAGEN, J.H.G., COOSEN, J. & HAAS, H.A. (1986). Interaction between seston quantity and quality and benthic suspension feeders in the Oosterschelde, the Netherlands. *Ophelia* 26, 385-399.

SOO, S.L. (1967). Fluid dynamics of Multiphase Systems. Blaisdell, Mass.

SORNIN, J.M. (1983). Influence de la biodéposition sur les propriétés rhéologiques des vases. *Journal de la Recherche Océanographique* 8, 115-123.

SPRUNG, M. & ROSE, U. (1988). Influence of food size and food quantity on the feeding of the mussel *Dreissena polymorpha*. *Oecologia* 77, 526-532.

SPUNGIN, B., AVOLIO, J., ARDEN, S. & SATIR, P. (1987). Dynein arm attachment probed with a non-hydrolyzable ATP analog: Structural evidence for patterns of activity. *Journal of Molecular Biology* 197, 671-677.

STASEK, C.R. (1962). Aspects of ctenidial feeding in immature bivalves. *The Veliger* 5, 78-79.

STASEK, C.R. (1965). Feeding and particle-sorting in *Yoldia ensifera* (Bivalvia: Protobranchia) with notes on other nuculanids. *Malacologia* 2, 349-366.

STEBBING, A.R.D. & DILLY, P.N. (1972). Some observations on living *Rhabdopleura compacta* (Hemichordata). *Journal of the Marine Biological Association of the United Kingdom* 52, 443-448.

STEFANO, G.B. & AIELLO, E. (1975). Histofluorescent localization of serotonin and dopamine in the nervous system and gill of *Mytilus edulis* (Bivalvia). *Biological Bulletin of the Marine Biological Laboratory, Woods Hole* 141, 141-156.

STEFANO, G.B., CATAPANE, E.J. & STEFANO, J.M. (1977). Temperature dependent ciliary rhythmicity in *Mytilus edulis* and the effects of monoaminergic agents on its manifestation. *Biological Bulletin of the Marine Biological Laboratory, Woods Hole* 153, 618-629.

STENTA, M. (1903). Zur Kenntniss der Strömungen im Mantelraume der Lamellibranchiaten. *Arbeiten aus dem Zoologischen Institut der Universität in Wien* 14, 211-240.

STEPHENS, G.C. (1988). Epidermal amino acid transport in marine invertebrates. *Biochemica et Biophysica Acta* 947, 113-138.

STRATHMANN, R.R. & LEISE, E. (1979). On feeding mechanisms and clearance rates of molluscan veligers. *Biological Bulletin of the Marine Biological Laboratory, Woods Hole* 157, 524-535.

STRATHMANN, R.R., JAHN, T.L. & FONSECA, J.R.C. (1972). Suspension feeding by marine invertebrate larvae: clearance of particles by ciliated bands of a rotifer, pluteus, and trochophore. *Biological Bulletin of the Marine Biological Laboratory, Woods Hole* 142, 505-519.

TAGHON, G.L. (1981). Beyond selection: optimal ingestion rate as a function of food value. *The American Naturalist* 118, 202-214.

TAMADA, K. & FUJIKAWA, H. (1957). The steady two-dimensional flow of viscous fluid at low Reynolds numbers passing through an infinite row of equal parallel circular cylinders. *Quarterly Journal of Mecanical and Applied Mathematics* 10, 425-432.

TAYLOR, A.C. (1976). Burrowing behaviour and anaerobiosis in the bivalve *Arctica islandica*. *Journal of the Marine Biological Association of the United Kingdom* 56, 95-109.

TENORE, K.R., GOLDMAN, J.C. & CLARNER, J.P. (1973). The food chain dynamics of the oyster, clam, and mussel in an aquaculture food chain. *Journal of Experimental Marine Biology and Ecology* 12, 157-165.

THEISEN, B.F. (1982). Variation in size of gills, labial palps, and adductor muscle in *Mytilus edulis* L. (bivalvia) from Danish waters. *Ophelia* 21, 49-63.

THOMPSON, R.J. & BAYNE, B.L. (1972). Active metabolism associated with feeding in the mussel *Mytilus edulis* L. *Journal of Experimental Marine Biology and Ecology* 9, 111-124.

THOMPSON, R.J. & BAYNE, B.L. (1974). Some relationships between growth, metabolism and food in the mussel *Mytilus edulis*. *Marine Biology* 27, 317-326.

THOMPSON, T.E. (1959). Feeding in nudibranch larvae. *Journal of the Marine Biological Association of the United Kingdom* 38, 239-248.

THORSON, G. (1936). The larval development, growth and metabolism of Arctic marine bottom invertebrates. *Meddelelser om Grønland* 100, No. 6, 1-155.

THORSON, G. (1952). Zur jetzigen Lage der marinen Bodentier-Ökologie. *Verhandlungen der Deutschen Zoologischen Gesellschaft in Wilhelmshafen* 1951, 276-327.

REFERENCES

TIMMS, R.M. & MOSS, B. (1984). Prevention of growth of potentially dense phytoplankton populations by zooplankton grazing, in the presence of zooplanktivorous fish, in a shallow wetland ecosystem. *Limnology and Oceanography* 29, 472-486.

TWAROG, B.M. (1967). Factors influencing contraction and catch in *Mytilus* smooth muscle. *Journal of Physiology* 192, 847-856.

VAHL, O. (1972a). Efficiency of particle retention in *Mytilus edulis* L. *Ophelia* 10, 17-25.

VAHL, O. (1972b). Particle retention and relation between water transport and oxygen uptake in *Chlamys opercularis* (L.) (Bivalvia). *Ophelia* 10, 67-74.

VAHL, O. (1973a). Porosity of the gill, oxygen consumption and pumping rate in *Cardium edulis* (L.) (Bivalvia). *Ophelia* 10, 109-118.

VAHL, O. (1973b). Efficiency of particle retention in *Chlamys islandica* (O.F. Müller). *Astarte* 6, 21-25.

VERDUIN, J. (1969). Hard clam pumping rates: Energy requirements. *Science* 166, 1309-1310.

VERWEY, J. (1952). On the ecology of distribution of cockle and mussel in the Dutch Waddensea, their role in sedimentation and the source of their food supply. *Archives Néerlandaises de Zoologie* 10, 171-239.

VILLIERS, C.J. DE, ALLANSON, B.R. & HODGSON, A.N. (1989). The effect of temperature on the filtration rate of *Solen cylindraceus* (Hanley) (Mollusca: Bivalvia). *South African Journal of Zoology* 24, 11-17.

VOGEL, S. (1974). Current-induced flow through the sponge, *Halichondria*. *Biological Bulletin of the Marine Biological Laboratory, Woods Hole* 147, 443-456.

VOGEL, S. (1977). Current-induced flow through living sponges in nature. *Proceedings of the National Academy of Sciences* 74, 2069-2071.

VOGEL, S. (1981). Life in Moving Fluids. Willard Grant, Boston.

VONK, H.J. (1924). Verdauungsphagocytose bei den Austern. *Zeitschrift für vergleichende Physiologie* 1, 607-623.

WALLACE, J.B. & MALAS, D. (1976a). The fine structure of capture nets of larval Philopotamidae (Trichoptera), with special emphasis on *Dolophilodes distinctus*. *Canadian Journal of Zoology* 54, 1788-1802.

WALLACE, J.B. & MALAS, D. (1976b). The significance of the elongate, rectangular mesh found in capture nets of fine particle filter feeding Trichoptera larvae. *Archiv für Hydrobiologie* 77, 205-212.

WALLENGREN, H. (1905a). Zur Biologie der Muscheln. I. Die Wasserströmungen. *Lunds Universitets Årsskrifter* N.F. Afd. 2, Bd. 1, Nr. 2, pp. 1-64.

WALLENGREN, H. (1905b). Zur Biologie der Muscheln. II. Die Nahrungsaufnahme. *Lunds Universitets Årsskrifter* N.F. Afd. 2, Bd. 1, Nr. 3, pp. 1-58.

WALNE, P.R. (1972). The influence of current speed, body size and water temperature on the filtration rate of five species of bivalves. *Journal of the Marine Biological Association of the United Kingdom* 52, 345-374.

WALSHAW, A.C. & JOBSON, D.A. (1979). Mechanics of Fluids, 3. ed. Longman, London and New York.

WARD, J.E. & TARGETT, N.M. (1989). Influence of marine microalgal metabolites on the feeding behavior of the blue mussel *Mytilus edulis*. *Marine Biology* 101, 313-321.

[*133*]

WARREN, A.E. (1936). An ecological study of the sea mussel (*Mytilus edulis* Linn.). *Journal of the Biological Board of Canada* 2, 89-94.

WARREN, C.E. & DAVIS, G.E. (1967). Laboratory studies on the feeding, bioenergetics, and growth of fish. *In* The Biological Basis of Freshwater Fish Production (ed. S.D. Gerking), pp. 175-214. Blackwell, Oxford.

WELSCHMEYER, N.A. & LORENZEN, C.J. (1985). Chlorophyll budgets: Zooplankton grazing and phytoplankton growth in a temperate zone fjord and the Central Pacific Gyres. *Limnology and Oceanography* 30, 1-21.

WERNER, B. (1955). Über die Anatomie, die Entwicklung und Biologie des Veligers und der Veliconcha von *Crepidula fornicata* L. (Gastropoda Prosobranchia). *Helgoländer wissenschaftliche Meeresuntersuchungen* 5, 169-217.

WHITE, W.R. (1968). A method for measuring the pumping rate of mussels (*Mytilus edulis* (L)). Central Electricity Research Laboratories, Laboratory Note No. RD/L/N 116/68.

WHITEHEAD, A.N. (1926). Science and the Modern World. Cambridge University Press, London. *Reprinted* Free Association Books, London, 1985.

WHYTE, L.L., WILSON, A.G. & WILSON, D. (1969). Hierarchical Structures. Elsevier, New York.

WIDDOWS, J. (1973). The effects of temperature on the metabolism and activity of *Mytilus edulis*. *Netherlands Journal of Sea Research* 7, 387-398.

WIDDOWS, J. (1978). Combined effects of body size, food concentration and season on the physiology of *Mytilus edulis*. *Journal of the Marine Biological Association of the United Kingdom* 58, 109-124.

WIDDOWS, J. & BAYNE, B.L. (1971). Temperature acclimation of *Mytilus edulis* with reference to its energy budget. *Journal of the Marine Biological Association of the United Kingdom* 51, 827-843.

WIDDOWS, J. & HAWKINS, A.J.S. (1989). Partitioning of rate of heat dissipation by *Mytilus edulis* into maintenance, feeding, and growth components. *Physiological Zoology* 62, 764-784.

WIDDOWS, J. & JOHNSON, D. (1988). Physiological energetics of *Mytilus edulis*: Scope for growth. *Marine Ecology Progress Series* 46, 113-121.

WIDDOWS, J., DONKIN, P., SALKELD, P.N., CLEARY, J.J., LOWE, D.M., EVANS, S.V. & THOMSON, P.E. (1984). Relative importance of environmental factors in determining physiological differences between two populations of mussels (*Mytilus edulis*). *Marine Ecology Progress Series* 17, 33-47.

WILDISH, D.J. (1977). Factors controlling marine and estuarine sublittoral macrofauna. *Helgoländer wissenschaftliche Meeresuntersuchungen* 30, 445-454.

WILDISH, D.J. & KRISTMANSON, D.D. (1984). Importance to mussels of the benthic boundary layer. *Canadian Journal of Fishery and Aquatic Sciences* 41, 1618-1625.

WILDISH, D.J. & KRISTMANSON, D.D. (1985). Control of suspension feeding bivalve production by current speed. *Helgoländer Meeresuntersuchungen* 39, 237-243.

WILDISH, D.J., KRISTMANSON, D.D., HOAR, R.L., DeCOSTE, A.M., McCORMICK, S.D. & WHITE, A.W. (1987). Giant scallop feeding and growth responses to flow. *Journal of Experimental Marine Biology and Ecology* 113, 207-220.

REFERENCES

WILLIAMS, G.C. (1966). Adaptation and Natural Selection. Princeton University Press, Princeton, New Jersey.

WINTER, J.E. (1973). The filtration rate of *Mytilus edulis* and its dependence on algal concentration, measured by a continuous automatic recording apparatus. *Marine Biology* 22, 317-328.

WINTER, J.E. (1974). Growth in *Mytilus edulis* using different types of food. *Berichte der Deutschen wissenschaftlichen Kommission für Meeresforschung* 23, 360-375.

WINTER, J.E. (1976). Feeding experiments with *Mytilus edulis* L. II. The influence of suspended silt in addition to algal suspensions on growth. *10th European Symposium on Marine Biology, Ostend, Belgium*, September 17-23, 1975, Vol. 1, pp. 583-600.

WINTER, J.E. (1978). A review on the knowledge of suspension-feeding in lamellibranchiate bivalves, with special reference to artificial aquaculture systems. *Aquaculture* 13, 1-33.

WINTER, J.E. & LANGTON, R.W. (1976). Feeding experiments with *Mytilus edulis* L. at small laboratory scale. I. The influence of the total amount of food ingested and food on growth. *10th European Symposium on Marine Biology, Ostend, Belgium*, September 17-23, 1975, Vol. 1, pp. 565-581.

WINTER, J.E., ACEVEDO, M.A. & NAVARRO, J.M. (1984). Quempillén estuary, an experimental oyster cultivation station in southern Chile. Energy balance in *Ostrea chilensis*. *Marine Ecology Progress Series* 20, 151-164.

WOODGER, J.H. (1930-31). The 'concept of organism' and the relation between embryology and genetics. *Quarterly Review of Biology* 5, 1-22, 438-463; 6, 178-207.

WRIGHT, R.T., COFFIN, R.B., ERSING, C.P. & PEARSON, D. (1982). Field and laboratory measurements of bivalve filtration of natural marine bacterioplankton. *Limnology and Oceanography* 27, 91-98.

WRIGHT, S.H. (1987). Alanine and taurine transport by the gill epithelium of a marine bivalve: effect of sodium on influx. *Journal of Membrane Biology* 95, 37-45.

YONGE, C.M. (1923-24). Studies on the comparative physiology of digestion. I. The mechanism of feeding, digestion and assimilation in the lamellibranch *Mya*. *British Journal of Experimental Biology* 1, 15-63.

YONGE, C.M. (1926-27). Structure and physiology of the organs of feeding and digestion in *Ostrea edulis*. *Journal of the Marine Biological Association of the United Kingdom* 14, 295-386.

YONGE, C.M. (1935). On some aspects of digestion in ciliary feeding animals. *Journal of the Marine Biological Association of the United Kingdom* 20, 341-346.

YONGE, C.M. (1947). The pallial organs in the aspidobranch Gastropoda and their evolution throughout the Mollusca. *Philosophical Transactions of the Royal Society, London* Series B, 232, 443-518.

YORK, B. & TWAROG, B.M. (1973). Evidence for the release of serotonin by relaxing nerves in molluscan muscle. *Comparative Biochemistry and Physiology* 44A, 423-430.

YOUNG, C.M. & BRAITHWAITE, L.F. (1980). Orientation and current-induced flow in the stalked ascidian *Styela montereyensis*. *Biological Bulletin of the Marine Biological Laboratory, Woods Hole* 159, 428-440.

Index

BIVALVE FILTER FEEDING:
HYDRODYNAMICS, BIOENERGETICS, PHYSIOLOGY AND ECOLOGY

Typeset in Sabon by Olsen & Olsen
Printed by Special-Trykkeriet Viborg a-s
Bound by Birger Sandersens Bogbinderi
Computer graphics by Olsen & Olsen.
Acknowledgement is due to the following authors and publishers
for permission to use figures for computer-processing and publication:
Figure 1A, 17, 18. Pergamon Press, Oxford
Figure 1B. G. Owen & J.M. McCrae / Royal Society, London
Figure 2, 19. Ophelia Publications, Helsingør
Figure 3. J.A. Allen / Royal Society, London
Figure 4, 5, 12, 20, 21, 22, 24a, 24b, 25. Inter-Research, Amelinghausen
Figure 7, 8, 10, 13. Springer-Verlag, Heidelberg
Figure 9. T. Kiørboe & F. Møhlenberg / Inter-Research, Amelinghausen
Figure 14. P. Famme *et al.* / Springer-Verlag, Heidelberg
Figure 15. F. Møhlenberg & H.U. Riisgård / Ophelia Publications, Helsingør
Figure 16. H.U. Riisgård & F. Møhlenberg / Springer-Verlag, Heidelberg
Figure 26. B. Clemmesen / Springer-Verlag, Heidelberg
Figure 29. K. Hamburger *et al.* / Springer-Verlag, Heidelberg
Figure 31. Plenum Press, New York
Figure 32. B. Barker Jørgensen / Oikos, Lund